*Slightly*

# A HOUSE IN FLANDERS

SLIGHTLY FOXED PAPERBACKS

# A HOUSE IN FLANDERS

Michael Jenkins

First published by Souvenir Press in 1992

First published, with the addition of new material,
by Slightly Foxed in 2010
in a limited edition of 2,000 copies
Paperback edition 2013

Slightly Foxed Ltd
53 Hoxton Square
London N1 6PB

A CIP catalogue record for this book is available from the British Library.

ISBN 978-1-906562-44-1

Printed by Smith Settle, Yeadon, West Yorkshire

For Maxine, Catherine and Nicholas

# Contents

Quelque autre te dira d'une plus forte voix,
Les faits de tes aïeux et les vertus des rois,
Je vais t'entretenir de moindres aventures.

La Fontaine,
Letter to the Dauphin

## *Preface*

In the extreme northern part of France lies the plain of Flanders, a great fertile expanse rolling inland from the sea until it meets a chain of conical hills which, strung out like a necklace of beads, runs north over the frontier to Belgium and southwards in the direction of Picardy. The plain is liberally dotted with prosperous-looking farms, whose thatched roofs and brick walls merge easily into the landscape while villages with massive church towers look down from the hills over woods and carefully husbanded fields. The magnificent skies remind you that if you are in France this is at the same time the Low Countries.

I was fourteen when I first came to the house on the edge of the plain. Some epidemic at school had, as was not unusual in those days, closed the establishment in the early summer, and my parents took the opportunity to despatch me for several months to 'the aunts in Flanders', mythical creatures as far as I was concerned, who had last been visited, I believe, by my father some time in the Thirties. Despite a French ancestry on my mother's side we were not related to the family and my parents had always been vague, deliberately I now think, about the origins of our connection with them.

Ever since I could remember I had been dimly aware of the

9

existence of the aunts and their great house in France not far from the border with Belgium. My parents had stayed with the family when travelling in northern France shortly after their marriage, but my father was not a Francophile and in any case the war severed all contact during years when I might have been curious to discover more about them. If stimulated, however, he would relate lively if not always charitable stories concerning the eccentricities of *les vieilles demoiselles* as he liked to call them; while my mother had retained a strong impression of the beauty of the place and the kindness shown to her, a comparative stranger, on her one brief visit. It was she who on impulse decided to write to the venerated head of the family, Tante Yvonne, with the suggestion that I might spend that summer at the house, and she received almost by return a welcoming and affectionate reply, coupled with the warning that I would be unlikely to have any companions of my own age. 'We are all by now, I fear, rather old, but we will do our best to amuse him and I feel sure he will find plenty to do here,' she wrote. In a few stately phrases she added that it would be a privilege to meet the next generation and to renew the relationship between our two families.

When the time came to leave home and make my way alone by boat and train to an unknown destination, I confess I felt distinctly queasy. But as I passed through the brick gateway perched on the front seat of an ancient black Citroën beside Joseph, the gardener who doubled as chauffeur, and saw behind the trees the long façade of the house, I believe I had some premonition that a new life was about to unfold.

And if after only a day the world I had left behind seemed already remote, within weeks I no longer knew which was reality, the coldness and austerity of my existence in post-war England, or the dense fabric of extended family by which I was embraced, and within whose lives I had become entwined.

As I discovered this new domain and made it my own, the long days ran into each other, forming a seamless web of time. Indeed, when I look back from this distance, it is as if everything had happened at once, a distillation of place and people never to be repeated. Only at the end did I come to understand that a world so complete and self-contained can be made to seem both an Elysium and a place of confinement; for one person a source of security and love, a shelter from outside, while for another giving rise to feelings of frustration and claustrophobia. But by then I was too involved to be dispassionate, or tolerant of any such sentiment. This was not the last occasion in my life when I would have given everything for time to stand still; and although I knew that such a state of permanence was unattainable, this realisation only led me to desire it all the more passionately.

For many years I have felt the need to write about my experiences that summer. The memory of them has lain in the recesses of my mind, slowly taking shape like a piece of coral under the sea, and occasionally brought to the surface by some chance phrase or encounter. Then a letter, recently received from one of the great-nieces of Tante Yvonne, who was seeking information about her last years, persuaded me that I should delay no longer. But as soon as I started to relive those days I realised that I had been composing this book off and on for more than half of my life, and the past and the present became one.

## I  *Tante Yvonne*

The old lady is seated at one end of the long table in the dining-room absorbed in some accounts, glasses perched on her nose. With the outstretched forefinger of her left hand, circled by a large ring, she holds down the paper while with her right she is scratching some figures using an oversized pen. A large bow of lace round her neck gives a touch of style, almost of coquetry to her dress, belying her expression of intense concentration. On the wall behind her hangs a portrait of her father, a bearded patriarch, while the shadow falling across the table is unmistakably that of her sister Lise who must be reading by the windows.

The picture was taken one summer afternoon by Tante Yvonne's nephew Bob, a keen photographer, possibly while I was sitting only a few feet away in my favourite place, the steps leading from the dining-room to the gravel terrace which ran the whole length of the house's southern side. From there you could look down over the lawn and a white bridge which crossed a small ornamental expanse of water, and beyond to a slope of fields gradually dropping into the plain. On a clear day you saw a great distance, while some trick of the light would make individual objects on the plain, such as trees or grazing animals, stand out with a startling clarity. A muddy cobbled road ran from one cluster of farms to the next, finally disappearing over the horizon in the direction of the local market town.

The prospect from the other side of the house, known as 'the village side', was quite different. Identical steps led from the front door, this time to a drive running into the same little road, which by now had meandered up from the plain and was passing the front of the house on its way to the village. Here the fields rose so steeply that the village walls appeared to be just above you. But if you walked up the footpath which ran from the chapel at the end of the drive and through the pasture to the village, it was ten energetic minutes before you were passing under one of the thick arches into the square, out of breath and very ready to rest for a moment on the stone bench set into the wall of the church.

Since I was invariably the first person about in the mornings I had appropriated the steps to the terrace as a vantage point from which both to command a view over the plain and to follow what was happening indoors. Beneath my feet a swastika, roughly carved with a soldier's knife, was a relic of the not so distant German occupation of the house. I would sit, with the stout black labrador Mardi stretched out beside me, usually reading a book recommended to me by one of the aunts, or gazing at the view while, like Mardi, keeping an ear cocked for sounds indoors. A creaking followed by a crash of shutters against the wall meant that Tante Lise was opening the house on her morning round; a rattle of the glass panes in the front door heralded the departure of her niece Madeleine to shop in the village; while the shuffling feet on the stairs signalled the descent of Oncle Auguste, anxious to swallow his coffee and escape into the garden before his wife, Alice, could find some uncongenial task for him.

Mornings were always somnolent at the house. The aunts were not early risers and Zoë the cook would already be cutting up the vegetables for lunch as, one by one, they appeared at the door of the cavernous kitchen in search of sustenance. Only Lise was down before the others had stirred, preparing the first of several meals during the day for her cocker spaniel, taking fresh grass to her rabbits who had over the years progressively taken possession of the old stables in the courtyard, and laying a tray for her elder sister, Yvonne, with which she would painfully make her way upstairs at nine o'clock precisely.

Lise was so bent that you did not often see her face. She was also almost totally deaf. Her universe was confined to her

animals and her sister, whom she guarded with equal jealousy.
Too much company quickly tired her: she would shelter in
her room at the top of the house or in the kitchen, preferring to
eat with Zoë and Joseph, the gardener, except on Sundays
when, halfway through lunch, she would silently appear in the
dining-room and sit hunched over her plate at one end of the
long table, smiling kindly at the children perched on their
stools next to her and anxious to get away as soon as she
decently could.

It was Lise who habitually sought me out later in the
morning in order to summon me to Tante Yvonne who would
by then be ensconced in the room we called the *petit salon*.
This gave directly on to the dining-room and was where Tante
Yvonne spent most of her waking hours. It was furnished for
comfort rather than elegance: easy chairs, their upholstery
well worn, stood round the fireplace; curiously coloured prints
representing scenic views of China and Japan were grouped
untidily on the walls; and in one corner stood a chipped
upright piano, which only Tante Thérèse, Yvonne's youngest
sister, regularly found the courage to play. On a round table in
the window stood a few ornaments and several packs of cards,
while at the back of the room a desk with a high top was used
by Madeleine to keep the house and farm papers. A door by
the desk opened into the library, a friendly retreat which was
lined with sagging bookshelves containing rows of heavily
bound volumes, and over which stuffed birds presided on
wooden pedestals.

These daily morning conversations with Tante Yvonne had

been initiated during my first week in the house under the pretext of improving my French, although thanks to my mother's efforts my understanding of the language was already rather better than that of a conventional English schoolboy. In practice Yvonne relished the opportunity my captive presence gave her to exercise her not inconsiderable talents as a raconteur: at times she would delve back into her past, exploring long-forgotten byways of family history. I never tired of the story of how her grandfather, a clever engineer from Picardy, came north to drain the marshes on the coast and, having acquired some of the reclaimed land for himself, decided to build a country house in the lee of the biggest hill on the plain. In his twenties and only just married, he designed the house in secret from his wife, driving her past it one day in the spring of 1840 and waiting expectantly for the question, 'Who lives in this magnificent place?' He was not disappointed. 'We do, my dear,' he is said to have replied as their carriage turned in at the gates. Fortunately she approved, for in the same year they moved into their new property and a few months later their first son, Gustave, was born. Successful management enabled father and son to build up a considerable estate of farms until Gustave and his wife were brutally struck down in their forties by typhoid fever and died within a month of each other, leaving six orphaned children, having lost two others in infancy. Yvonne at twenty was the eldest; she did not hesitate to take charge of her siblings.

On other occasions Tante Yvonne enjoyed telling me anecdotes or making unflattering comments on her relations, often delivered from behind her hand in elaborate stage whispers as they went back and forth past the open drawing-room door. Her chair was set at the window from where she could look over the plain, following with a critical eye the activity on the farms and issuing instructions between seemingly endless games of patience.

As I quickly discovered, it was not altogether easy living in a house with six strong-willed women. As an outsider you had to be sensitive to the cross-currents and know how to avoid reviving long-buried family arguments. I noticed that each aunt had her own territory and was careful to keep to her own self-appointed duties. Tante Florence supervised the kitchen and, having once owned a restaurant in Paris, liked to surprise us with the occasional over-elaborate lunch or dinner which left her sisters-in-law grumbling about the richness of the food. Tante Alice organised the fruit-picking and made the jams and preserved fruit. Tante Thérèse and her companion Mathilde worked together on certain flower-beds in the garden which only they were permitted to touch. Accompanied by Thérèse's numerous grandchildren, their arrival every June from the house they shared 'in the south' – in fact no farther than Tours – was felt to mark the change of the season as did their departure again at the end of September. All deferred to Yvonne as the eldest sister and recognised head of the family.

Tante Yvonne accepted the attentions paid to her as part of the natural order. She was waited on hand and foot by Lise, and I also rapidly became aware that she was accustomed to having her *obiter dicta*, incisive as they often were, treated on all sides as if engraved on tablets of stone. Only gradually did I learn of the sacrifices she had made throughout her long life for the sake of her family. Now in her mid-eighties, she radiated calm and authority. Small, almost squat, she moved slowly with the help of a silver-capped cane. Her expression was usually kindly, but her hooded eyes were full of intelligence and wit, and her glance was still penetrating.

Her days followed an unvarying routine. In the mid-morning she would make a slow progress to the ground floor, stepping carefully backwards in order to avoid an attack of vertigo, down the long staircase which was lined with now rather shabby *toile de Jouy* wallpaper depicting hunting scenes, and then take up her regular position behind the round table in the salon overlooking the terrace. This was the hour when she liked to transact business with Madeleine who kept the accounts, or with any of the farmers who chose to come to her with their problems. Before lunch members of the family would assemble and greet her while she played a first game of patience. Lunch, in the adjacent dining-room, was punctually at one and she presided firmly over the large and often noisy table. In the afternoon she would doze in her chair and then take a short walk on the terrace if the weather was fine, sometimes, on particularly warm days, even drinking tea under one of the great beech trees on the lawn. At seven she would return up the staircase to her room in order to change her dress for dinner. One sensed that it was the evening Tante Yvonne enjoyed best, with the family round her conversing about the day, and the rhythm of the house slowing to the pace at which she led her own life.

On Sunday mornings Mass was often said in the small salon so that Tante Yvonne, no longer able comfortably to walk as far as the family chapel at the end of the drive, could take communion from a former parish priest, Abbé Philippe, who had retired to a cottage under the village walls. His arrival was announced by the purring of his *mobilette* on which he would ride unsteadily down the hill, his black cassock flapping behind him. Father Philippe evidently enjoyed this weekly ritual. In the absence of Bob, who usually assisted him during the service, he would ask me to read the responses and to hand round at the appropriate moment an old biscuit box, embossed with the arms of an English regiment – a relic of the First War – in which Lise chose to keep the unconsecrated wafers. He looked forward perhaps even more to the lunch for which he habitually stayed and where, I noticed, he helped himself generously to every course. His little eyes would twinkle behind his glasses as he cut a large portion of his favourite pork *rillettes* while complaining with a sigh about the culinary shortcomings of his housekeeper.

Tante Yvonne did not confine her proprietary interest to her immediate family; it extended to everyone with whom she had dealings and certainly included the five or six tenant farmers who worked the fields on the plain below the house. If her comments and interference were not always appreciated, these *paysans* knew that they had a fair and understanding proprietor who could usually be persuaded to defer payment of rent or even waive it altogether in cases of hardship.

One morning a few weeks after my arrival, Yvonne remarked that the roof of a barn on one of the larger farms in the plain below should by now have been repaired. 'Go and ask Ivan from me why he is delaying,' she instructed me. 'Ivan the Terrible' was what she liked to call the oldest and surliest of the tenants, as he was perfectly aware from the generations of children who had addressed him as Monsieur Ivan. Anticipating only too well his reaction to interference from 'Mademoiselle Yvonne', I did not relish this errand. I set off reluctantly after lunch down a little track which wound through the wheat and barley fields, and was known, grandiloquently but obscurely, as the Duke's Path. I found every excuse to dawdle on the way. Mardi had to be kept on a lead, in case she ran wild over the fields, disturbing the game before the shooting season. But as it was hot I set her free when we reached the stream that crossed our path and she paddled up and down the water, happy to cool off while I sat on the rail of the wooden bridge and looked back at the big rectangular house whose severe façade was alleviated by a metal canopy over the central steps and by the great windows that ran the entire length of the terrace. Now most of the shutters were closed as the house slumbered in the afternoon sun, while above it were silhouetted the village roofs and the oversized tower of the church. The blue of a cloudless summer sky, the yellow fields of grain and the green of the trees and of the grass sloping down from the terrace made strong, almost crude contrasts of colour, dramatic enough to catch the eye of even a fourteen-year-old boy. As I watched, one of the glass doors on to the terrace swung open to reveal the angular figure of

Tante Alice who paused on the steps before making her slow way to the massive beech tree on the lawn under which the aunts liked to play bridge on warm afternoons. She was followed by Florence, Mathilde and Thérèse. From my distance the old ladies looked like paper cut-outs in a child's theatre as in slow motion they headed across the grass wearing an arresting collection of summer hats.

It was time to face Ivan. I called Mardi and walked on down the path, turning into a red brick courtyard with a low, gabled farmhouse at the far end, and stables and byres, also of red brick, running down each side from the entrance. The farm would have been attractive but for a large pit filled with manure which took up the whole centre of the yard and was an equal source of flies and ripe smells. A clattering in the stables led me to the farmer, who was bent over a tractor. Nervously I delivered my message, but to my relief he did not after all appear upset.

'All the fault of the Co-operative,' he shouted cheerfully, grimacing with his thick lips. 'You tell Mademoiselle Yvonne that if she wants to see her roofs repaired she must get them to send us the materials when we are ready. But they have promised a delivery for next week. Now, young man, let me offer you something.'

I followed his stocky figure into a dark kitchen where he motioned me to sit at a table covered with a greasy plastic cloth. He produced two glasses and a familiar bottle of watery brown liquid which, although universally drunk in the region, bore only a passing resemblance to beer.

'Look, I'm glad you've come, I have something I want you to give to Mademoiselle Yvonne.' He looked at me sharply and, going to a dresser in the farthest corner of the room, rummaged in one of the drawers, extracting an object wrapped in cloth which he brought over and laid on the table in front of me. Inside was a large pocket watch, the glass discoloured but intact, the casing dull and black. 'Silver,' he grunted, 'I found it last week in the long field. And look here.' He pressed a knob and the back swung open to reveal a tarnished interior on which the initial 'A' was engraved.

'Monsieur Antoine,' he explained, 'he was the youngest of them. He was a real card, always in trouble but always laughing. He could get away with anything; and he did.' Sweating profusely Ivan pushed his cap back on his bald head and wiped his forehead with his sleeve. 'We all liked him, and of course they loved him up at the house. They took it really badly when he was killed in the Great War; and they could certainly have done with him after it. See here, I don't want to upset Mademoiselle Yvonne. So you give this watch to her very quietly, just from me; she will know what to do with it.'

Ten minutes later I was on the path moving uphill towards the house. The aunts had vanished into the shadow of the trees. The only sign of movement was a small boy tricycling unsteadily along the gravel terrace. As I watched he toppled over, but I was still too far off to hear his cries.

That evening after dinner I sat down next to Tante Yvonne at her round table in the drawing-room and offered to play a match of *dames* with her. The rules were subtly different from those of draughts with which I was familiar, and she beat me several times before I finally won a game. I told her that Ivan would begin his repairs the next week and then said I would like to help her upstairs when she retired, as I had something to show her.

It took us a long time to mount the staircase, but after many pauses during which Tante Yvonne leaned heavily on her cane, we finally reached her bedroom. The shutters were closed and the dark purple curtains drawn, although it was a warm night. The bed, in an alcove, was surmounted by a vast framed crucifix on a velvet background, while photographs of parents, brothers and sisters hung on a wall directly by the pillows. Tante Yvonne subsided into an armchair and looked expectantly at me. I took the watch from my pocket and handed it to her, explaining that the farmer had wanted me to give this to her privately.

Yvonne turned the battered and tarnished object over uncomprehendingly until she succeeded in opening the back and saw the initial. She sat, her head bent and the watch in her lap, so still that I wondered whether she was falling asleep. At last she looked up, and I was disconcerted to see that her eyes were wet with tears. To cover my embarrassment I turned to leave her, but she reached out and put a hand on my arm.

'I remember it well,' she said, smiling. 'We gave this to my brother on his thirtieth birthday. He was so upset when he lost it in the fields. And two years later he was dead.'

She gestured me to sit in a chair opposite her and there was a long silence while she looked alternately at the watch and, with a reflective but affectionate expression, at myself. Since my arrival I had more than once caught the same glance and on each occasion it had fleetingly puzzled me; I had the sensation of being appraised, perhaps even compared with someone.

'Now I would like you to do something for me,' said Yvonne at last. 'I want you to clean this watch – make the silver really shine – and then take it to our Christian as a present from Mademoiselle Yvonne.' She lowered her voice and leaned forward. 'It will be a secret between us.

'And I suppose you had better know why,' she went on, noting my surprise with amusement. For Christian was the amiable but half-witted labourer who was supposed to help Joseph in the garden, and lived on his own in a small cottage at one end of the property. I would come across him fishing for carp in the lake, or standing silently under the trees, looking out over the plain as if lost in some unfathomable meditation. He never did much beyond trimming the occasional hedge or mowing a patch of grass – the lawns behind and in front of the house were evidently thought to be too much for him. He had, as it were, a walk-on part in the scheme of things, a state with which both he and his employers appeared to be content. My attempts at conversation with Christian never managed to advance beyond a good-natured greeting and a muttered phrase about the weather.

'My brother Antoine liked, I'm afraid, to enjoy himself

with the young ladies in the village,' said Tante Yvonne even more quietly. 'Unfortunately he never thought of the consequences. He needed a father or a mother, and had neither; I did my best, although it was not much. For ten years I tried to persuade him to marry and settle down but I never succeeded.' She sighed. 'Anyway, his death was a shock to us, but not only to us, it appeared. A girl whose family farmed near the Boulogne road came to see me with her father and said that her baby was Antoine's. No one could prove it, but I thought we must help, so I supported her. At least she did not call her son Antoine!' Yvonne gave a dry little laugh.

'She insisted on keeping the boy even when she saw that he was not quite normal. Later she married and took him away to Amiens, but a few years ago she died and I brought Christian back here. I have tried to tell him about his father but I do not know whether he understands. Zoë gives him his meals and he loves this place. Our brother Auguste does not like me to say so, but you can see that he is one of us. So that is why he must have the watch, even though I think it will never work again.' She looked up and patted me on the arm. 'Family secrets, everyone has them,' she smiled. 'There would have been a problem if Antoine had lived, but I still miss him after all these years. Now I must say my prayers.'

Holding on to the arm of her chair she got awkwardly to her feet. A moth fluttered out of the heavy curtains and settled on the carpet in front of her. I felt proud to be the recipient of Tante Yvonne's confidences; it was as if I had passed some test.

I picked up the watch and, promising to make it shine like new, slipped away to my little room on the floor above. Opening the window I leaned on the sill and breathed in with pleasure the fresh night air. I could hear the sheep moving in the darkness of the field below, and see points of light shining from the farms across the plain. But Christian's cottage was hidden in the trees.

Two days later I went in search of him. It was midday and I wanted to complete my mission in his house rather than somewhere outside. It was, I felt, more fitting; besides, I was curious to see how he lived. The long, low cottage had at some stage been divided into two halves: Zoë now had one, and Christian the other. A number of fruit trees, some ragged grass and a bed for vegetables comprised the garden while a wooden butt, with a coat of green weed on the surface of the water, stood by the door.

I knocked, but hearing no response cautiously pressed the latch and looked inside. Christian was sitting at a table with a bowl of soup and a large bottle of beer in front of him. He grinned and said, '*Bonjour,*' when he saw me, but showed no surprise and remained seated. My eyes took in a stove, a chest and cupboard and an armchair in the dark room which, despite its sparse furnishing, did not feel uncomfortable. I paused in the doorway and, since Christian still made no gesture, walked in, drawing a chair up to the table and seating myself opposite him.

'Christian, I have a gift for you from Mademoiselle Yvonne.' I reached into my pocket and brought out the now gleaming if still somewhat tarnished watch, unwrapping it carefully from my handkerchief. Christian's spoon, half-way to his mouth, froze and was then lowered. I opened the back to show him the initial and pushed the watch across the table. For a moment he looked at me without expression: he had, I noticed, the rough complexion of someone who spends every season outdoors. He was losing his hair, but his eyes were a bright blue. Then he reached out his hand and picked up the watch.

'Look,' I said, '"A". It belonged to . . .' I did not think it right to say 'your father', so after hesitating I decided on 'Monsieur Antoine'.

'That's right,' he said. He paused and repeated 'Monsieur Antoine' and then 'Antoine'. He looked knowingly at me. 'I thank Mademoiselle Yvonne,' he said in a low voice, putting the watch carefully by his plate. He picked up his spoon again. 'Later,' he stated, 'you may come fishing.' With this invitation I felt politely dismissed, and slipped quietly out and away up the path through the meadow.

## II  Tante Florence

The attic ran the entire length of the house, although it was divided into a number of rooms: some were former maids' bedrooms and had now become furniture and picture stores, and a large area was given over to broken trunks and suitcases which would never travel again but could still serve as receptacles for bric-à-brac accumulated over the years. Exploring the attic, preferably with one of the aunts, was a favourite occupation for me. Old photograph albums would spark a stream of anecdotes. The dressing-up box, with its clothes from the Thirties, brought back memories of great pre-war parties, the nostalgia being somehow increased by an old croquet set with its broken mallets and chipped wooden balls, and a pile of abandoned tennis racquets, whose strings in their curiously elongated heads had long since decayed. There was always the chance of finding some long-forgotten treasure, perhaps an old drawing or engraving, which could be brought downstairs, admired and then, if I wished, hung in my room.

Once, when I was in the attic on my own, I came across a sack still tied at the top but burst open on one side. It was filled with bundles of letters. Feeling a little guilty, I pulled the nearest one from its envelope. It was addressed simply 'Thérèse', and read:

> Picardy
> 16 September 1916
>
> My dearest sister,
>
> Yesterday we moved up to the front again. As usual, I cannot tell you exactly where we are and anyway it seems hardly to matter since one set of trenches looks much like another. Our companies have been entirely rebuilt since that last terrible attack but my men are in good spirits and we are ready to have another go at the Boches as soon as the order is given. The guns have stopped firing for once and it is wonderful to hear birds again: I am astonished that any are still here after such noise. I saw Antoine at the training camp three days ago: he was well and he is now positioned only a kilometre or so away. The mud, the smells and the flies are terrible but my worries are not here, they are with you. I just hope that

the enemy can be held at Ypres and that our village will be spared. Please take good care of my beloved Florence. My thoughts are with you all.

Your affectionate brother,
    Henri

Somehow I already sensed what the next letter would say, but I unfolded it with no less fascination.

Picardy
20 September 1916

My dearest Thérèse,

I know you will have already received by telegram the terrible news. I am writing this from the dressing station. I had a message this morning that Antoine had been wounded by a shell during yesterday's advance and I was at once given permission to leave the line and visit him. Our dear brother died at seven this morning, so I arrived too late. They will bury him, with five others from his company, later today. They have given me his disc and ring. He looked so peaceful that I do not think he can have suffered much.

I am still so shocked that I can find no words to measure our loss. It will be harder for you and for Yvonne and Lise alone in the house – I pray every day for you all and that we will somehow safely come through this cruel time. I know that God is watching over us.

Yesterday's fighting was long and hard, but we have

held the ground we took, and are to be relieved very soon. We are now all tired out but the enemy must be as exhausted as we are. I will write again as soon as I can. I am enclosing a note for you to send on to my darling Florence if you know how to reach her.

Your Henri

The next afternoon I took the two letters rather nervously to Tante Florence. She was sitting sewing in the window of the large upstairs drawing-room which she liked to use as her bedroom in the summer months. It ran from one side of the house to the other so that if you stood in the middle you could look both up at the village or, turning your head, out across the plain. The room was a jumble of half-completed garments scattered over tables and chairs, books lying open where they had been left half-read, and photographs, some framed, others stuck in mirrors or picture frames. A huge bed covered in cushions stood against the wall opposite the fireplace while a sedan chair, in an advanced state of decay, served in one corner as an incongruous receptacle for children's toys.

Florence was usually sewing or knitting: it added to her habitual serene, comfortable air which was only occasionally broken by bouts of frenzied activity when, for reasons she could never explain, she sought briefly to reverse the habits and routine of a lifetime. In the previous year she had without warning removed all her belongings and furniture to a cousin's apartment in Paris, only to return equally precipitately a few months later. Tante Yvonne was accustomed to these squalls.

'My sister-in-law is a placid sea, but when the wind is blowing it is better to make way for her,' she would say.

Tante Florence looked up at me calmly over her spectacles as I told her of my find. To my surprise, she showed no desire to read the letters, but putting down her work she looked reflectively out across the fields to the village walls.

'Poor Henri, he had a hard life,' she observed softly, 'first our long courtship, then the war, and then his illness and his struggle to find work. War is a terrible thing. The Great War brought us together and its consequences finally separated us. But we had many happy days.'

For the next hour Florence told me the story of her marriage. 'They were difficult times for us both,' she said. 'Neither of our families wanted us to marry. My father was a cultivated man – he loved books and music – but as one of Yvonne's tenants he was worried that I would not be accepted by the family; while they feared that without money or qualifications Henri would be unable to maintain a marriage with a dowerless girl as I was.'

But Yvonne had been on her brother's side, and with no father or mother it was the eldest sister's voice that counted.

'She was already running the house, the farms, and arranging the lives of her brothers and sisters for that matter. No wonder she never had time to marry herself. We were finally engaged in the summer of '14, but then the war came and we thought it better to wait until it was over. After all, no one believed the fighting would last beyond Christmas. How wrong we were!'

They had to endure a long and frustrating separation. Florence went to Paris, but to train as a nurse rather than study literature. Henri's regiment, having gained its spurs in the battle of the Marne, was transferred to eastern France in 1915, and from there to the Somme in 1916. Henri and Florence were able to meet in Paris or at the house during the early months of the war. Thereafter their respective periods of leave rarely coincided; indeed, so frequently was Florence moved with her mobile hospital that Henri could not often correspond directly with her.

Then, in October 1916, hard on the news of the death of Antoine, Yvonne received another telegram telling her that Henri had been wounded in action. By a lucky chance, Florence was at the house when this alarming message arrived. Its imprecision was disquieting: there was no indication of the nature of his injuries, nor where he was being cared for. Florence wasted no time. She was only too well aware of the appalling conditions in the mobile hospitals and dressing stations behind the battlefields and felt sure that Henri's life was at stake. Pulling all the many strings she had by this time acquired, she succeeded in reserving a bed in a Paris clinic and, using her nurse's pass, travelled to the eastern Somme in search of Henri. After three days she found him, lying still unattended in a small hospital near Amiens: he had been badly wounded in the left leg and was by now delirious. Within a day she was accompanying him on a train to Paris where at last he could be treated. The surgeons found that gangrene had already set in and the leg had to be amputated, but Henri's life was saved. Had he been left on the Somme he would surely have died.

His recovery was slow: it was many weeks before he was well enough to leave hospital and travel home to begin a long convalescence. When he arrived, early in 1917, he found the house and estate much changed. Staff officers from the British forces near Ypres had taken over some of the rooms and the outbuildings; soldiers were camped everywhere in the grounds, and the great lawns had been ploughed up to grow vegetables. The whole property resembled a barracks. Yvonne and Lise were living on the top floor of the house but Yvonne seemed strangely invigorated by the makeshift lives which had been thrust upon them.

Henri's only ambition now was to marry Florence as soon as he was well enough to do so. The world had changed violently and radically since the beginning of the war and the uncertainties about his future which had loomed so large in peacetime had now taken on universal proportions. Moreover peace seemed as far away as ever. Accordingly, in early November 1917 there was a small ceremony in the little chapel at the end of the drive. Yvonne acted as bridesmaid, and Henri's elder brother Auguste, now an artillery colonel and a miraculous survivor of Verdun, was best man. An old priest from the village officiated, and an English trumpeter blew a fanfare. As Henri limped on crutches back to the house with his bride, British troops were going into action thirty miles to the east at Passchendaele.

Henri had only another ten years to live. He never fully

recovered from his wound, nor was he able to find work and set up a household of his own. But he and Florence were installed in a cottage in the grounds and there they produced three children, two boys – Bob and François – and a daughter, Madeleine.

Florence sighed. 'My Madeleine was born a few months after Henri died. She was such a pretty child, but headstrong from the start and she needed a father.'

Personally I found Madeleine more than pretty: with her long blonde hair, blue eyes, and slim legs and figure, she was what my father, a connoisseur in these matters, would have called 'a real stunner' and for me she filled the house with light. Occasionally, however, she was subject to sudden and unpredictable changes of mood, a trait which she had perhaps inherited from her mother. Then she would become unaccountably irritable, almost sulky, snapping at anyone who crossed her path although never, I noticed, at Tante Yvonne.

'When Henri died I had many difficulties,' ended Florence quietly. 'There were those, like my sister-in-law Alice, who said they had been right all along and we should never have married. But Yvonne told me not to listen to them. She helped me buy my restaurant in Paris but I found it too difficult to run on my own. She adored her nephews and nieces and when I came back here she somehow helped me to provide for my children. I was proud that they returned her loyalty and affection by standing by this place when the Germans came. Now Madeleine works harder than any of us to keep everything running as Yvonne wants. I do not know what will happen when she marries Serge.'

This was a reference to Madeleine's long-standing engagement to a family friend who farmed his own land, his house lying in woods which covered a neighbouring hill. Serge came and went unobtrusively and was treated as if he was already a son-in-law; he was very tall and for me this somehow made his quiet and gentle manner all the more unexpected. I had also noticed that Madeleine was never over-excited by his presence; their relationship seemed to me to be more that of brother and sister.

I wanted to hear more about Florence's own family but I could see that she was tired after talking so long. I had in fact only a day to wait. The next morning, when I went to find Tante Yvonne for our talk before lunch, I discovered her deep in conversation with Florence and Madeleine. Yvonne was looking indignant: one hand knocked repeatedly on her table, the other held a typewritten letter.

'It is the old feud,' she was saying as I came in. 'Why will the village never leave us alone? But I will fight for our property as I always have. First the Germans, now the Communists.'

'Please keep calm, Yvonne,' said Florence gently, 'the municipality are only asking for one field. I am sure we can reach an agreement.'

'One field! They will start with my little finger and then take a whole arm. And look where they want to make their sports ground – at the end of the drive, almost directly under our windows. It is a deliberate provocation from that nephew of yours.

What he wants is unacceptable: I shall go and tell him so.'

Now Florence seemed more worried. 'Would it not be better for me to talk to Rémy? He may be the Mayor, but he is my brother's son.'

'You know what he thinks of you and of all of us,' replied Yvonne. 'No, it is my duty as head of the family to see him.'

'Should we not have an alternative to offer them?' asked Madeleine, moving over to the desk in the corner on which a number of large maps lay unfolded. 'There must be other possibilities which they would have to consider.'

'Not one centimetre,' declared Yvonne, 'and he will hear that from me this afternoon. Madeleine, please ask Joseph to have the car ready at three o'clock and tell the Mayor's office that I will call – alone.'

After lunch Tante Yvonne went upstairs and shortly after appeared in a black dress and hat, more suited I thought to a funeral than to a business interview. Punctually at three, old Joseph drew up in the battered Citroën limousine and opened the rear door with a flourish worthy of the chauffeur of a Rolls-Royce. He had donned a peaked cap and a dark jacket which, with his usual rolling gait, gave him a somewhat nautical air. We all assembled on the steps to wave goodbye, as if Yvonne was leaving for a long journey. With painful deliberation, the old lady settled herself on the back seat. As the car vanished down the drive Florence remarked unhappily, 'They will both enjoy the fight, but no good will come of it. My nephew is as stubborn as she is.'

We went back into the drawing-room to wait. Florence

picked up her sewing. Madeleine began to study the survey again. Through the window I could see Oncle Auguste, in a straw hat and baggy trousers, attacking a bush by the lawn with a pair of garden shears. Several children ran along the terrace, shouting and laughing together, and then swooped on a sandpit under one of the trees like a flock of birds.

'Even when my brother was alive, Rémy never accepted us,' said Florence reflectively. 'Do you remember, Madeleine, how he always refused to come and play with the boys? He was determined not to be seen as part of this family. Then the Communists got hold of him during the war, when he was in the Resistance, and that was that. Now that he is Mayor he can make a lot of trouble for us if he chooses.'

An hour later we heard the car return and Tante Yvonne appeared in the drawing-room. She was breathing heavily and sat down without removing her hat.

'The man is impossible,' she said fiercely, 'he would not listen to reason. I spoke of his parents, I reminded him that he was part of our family. He would only say that the municipality had taken its decision. And he read me the law. If he wishes to behave this way I shall have to engage a lawyer.'

'That will be expensive and we may lose anyway,' said Madeleine firmly, 'but I know the law as well. If we can offer something else they have to justify rejecting it. I have two suggestions.'

She unfolded one of the maps; two grey heads and a blonde one bent over it. There followed a long discussion until finally Yvonne made a weary gesture.

'All right, but you two must talk to Rémy for I will not let him humiliate me further.' Florence looked, I thought, relieved by this decision.

The next morning Joseph drove Florence and her daughter to the village. They asked me to come with them in order to help with the maps. These were indeed heavy to carry, each being stored in a bulky wooden tube.

The Mairie was an elegant, eighteenth-century house on the village square, at the opposite end from the church. The façade was still badly cracked and pitted by shell splinters and bullets from the short battle for the village which had occurred in 1940. Laden with the wooden map cases I climbed the steps behind Florence and Madeleine in the posture of an Indian bearer. We were ushered down an echoing stone corridor which smelt strongly of beeswax, and without ceremony into the Mayor's office. Rémy stood up as we entered: he embraced neither his aunt nor his cousin, but shook hands with all three of us.

Rémy Dumoulin was short and stout with a square head and deep-set eyes. He gave an impression of alertness and energy, and his manner was brisk. Without preamble Madeleine explained that we had an alternative offer to make.

'I will listen to you but I fear you are wasting your time,' responded Rémy. 'My Council wishes to acquire this land and under the law we are entitled to do so, with fair compensation to you, of course. We have studied every possibility for the recreational facility, and this is the only one which adequately meets the needs of the village. I am sorry,' he added drily.

We unfolded the maps and spread them on his desk. Madeleine pointed to the two chosen spots and Rémy stared down at them, narrowing his eyes further, and tutting with his tongue.

'Won't do, I'm afraid: this one is too far from the village centre, and this one liable to flooding. Of course, if you insist I shall have to submit your proposals to my Council but I know they will be rejected.' He appeared to be enjoying himself.

Florence had been sitting silently on one side of the room; now she stirred.

'Rémy, I should like, please, to speak to you alone.' She motioned Madeleine and myself to the door. Rémy seemed about to object, but then shrugged his shoulders, looking pointedly at his watch and pushing the maps towards me.

'Very well, but I only have ten minutes,' he grumbled.

Madeleine and I found two straight-backed chairs in the empty corridor. She sat staring at the white wall in front of her, her legs tucked under the seat.

'You know that this is more than a quarrel over a field,' she said softly. 'God knows why, but Rémy is leading a group in the village which is determined to take as much from us as they can. My uncle always resented mother's marriage and he passed on to his son the same hostility towards us. You can see what Rémy is like: hard as granite and full of hate, too.'

It was not ten minutes but half an hour that elapsed before Florence emerged from the Mayor's office. Rémy, pale and unsmiling, stood in the doorway as she came towards us and said we could now leave. We followed her in silence until we came out on the steps of the Mairie and signalled to Joseph to bring up the car. The map cases weighed heavily on my arms.

'It will be all right,' said Florence with a sigh, 'he will take one of the alternatives.'

Once we were all three in the back of the Citroën Madeleine turned to her mother.

'How did you manage to persuade him?' she asked admiringly. 'He seemed so very determined to have his way.'

Florence gave a small, sad grimace. 'I reminded him, or thought I was reminding him, that Yvonne had probably saved his father's life in 1944. When the Germans were recruiting any able-bodied men, however old, they could find for labour in Germany, Yvonne brought my brother to the village house where she and Lise were then living, and told the neighbours that he was ill with typhoid fever. The soldiers who arrived at the door checked her story down the street, but preferred not to come in and see my brother for themselves. Had they done so and discovered the truth they would certainly have taken Yvonne away as well. And only one of that group of conscripts returned to France: the rest were killed by a direct hit from an Allied bomb on the factory where they were all working.

'Rémy has just told me that his father never explained to him precisely what risk Yvonne took for him. He may be right – my brother was a strange man. Nor of course has Yvonne ever spoken to him about those days. I am afraid she would regard what I have done as unworthy, so we must keep all this to ourselves.'

### III  Oncle Auguste

I was fond of Oncle Auguste. There were days, it is true, when he exhibited all the signs of extreme old age: he would forget to shave one side of his face, dress carelessly and drag his feet so much when he walked that Tante Yvonne once suggested to her brother that he could help with the housework by attaching floor polishers to his slippers. At these times he was always liable to punctuate long periods of silence at meals by lurching suddenly to his feet from behind the large carafe of red wine to which he helped himself liberally, looking round the long table and beginning or, who knows, ending a speech already delivered in his mind with the phrase, 'I raise my glass . . .' He never got further before Tante Alice tapped him on the arm with a 'not now, Auguste', and he subsided. This performance never failed to amuse his great-nephews and nieces clustered at the end of the table.

But Auguste also had his 'good' days when he appeared smart and alert. After lunch he would invite anyone he could find to accompany him on the 'big walk' around the grounds. Usually it was only I who responded to this invitation although Auguste's nephew Bob, who spent most weekends at the house, liked to escort him on Sunday afternoons. As opposed to the 'little walk' which involved no more than a turn on the gravel round the house and pond at the end of the lawn, the big walk took you along the confines of the property: through the meadow overlooking the plain to the wood, thence down the great avenue of lime trees to the lake that lay under the village walls, and back along the front drive, with a pause to say a prayer at the chapel if one of the more devout of the aunts was also with us.

We were engaged on this expedition one day when Auguste, seemingly casually, made me a revelation. As usual, we were resting after the first part of the walk on a wooden seat looking over the plain. In front of us some tall rusting poles surrounded what had once been a tennis court; the wire netting had long since vanished, and weeds and molehills now occupied its uneven surface. Glancing over his shoulder at an old garden shed behind us, Auguste remarked that his earliest memory was of accidentally shutting himself inside and being rescued by Yvonne.

'Always saved us when we were in trouble,' he remarked,

'she was mother and father to all five of us. When our parents both died of typhoid in '86 my unmarried Oncle Ernest moved here from Paris. But Yvonne was already in charge; it's been that way ever since.'

'Was that why she never married?' I asked. There were photographs of Yvonne in the house showing, I thought, a very attractive young girl.

Auguste gave me a sharp glance. 'Maybe, but of course you know the story?'

I shook my head and Auguste made a curious noise, somewhere between a snort and a laugh.

'She was more or less engaged to be married in '90 to an English officer. Two of them were staying with us here, on liaison with some military exercises in the north, I think. Both in love with her, if you ask me: and one of them proposed. She accepted him before he left, but on condition they waited at least three years. My brothers were still so young. So off he went to India. For a time we had no news. Then there was a letter saying he was marrying an English girl. After that she never looked elsewhere.' Auguste seemed animated rather than exhausted by this, for him, unusually long statement.

'What a shame! Who was he?' I asked.

Auguste paused for effect. Then, swinging round on the seat, he seized my arm.

'He was your grandfather, that's who he was. How about that!' he shouted, his eyes brilliant behind his glasses. He pulled at his moustache and grinned, evidently enjoying my astonishment.

A hundred questions crowded in, but Auguste's train of thought was already moving on and could not be halted.

'She refused to leave the property while we all grew up; even after the war when she could have done so she would not budge. We tried to persuade her to come to Lyons, Alice and I. But she said she was only happy here. She felt that one day she would be needed again . . . Of course if my brothers had lived . . . .' his voice trailed away and he began to mutter inaudibly. Then he lurched to his feet. 'We must go on!' he exclaimed, and side by side we walked slowly down the meadow. As we proceeded I attempted repeatedly to revert to the subject of my grandfather, but each time Auguste refused to be drawn, beyond the enigmatic comment that he, at any rate, had never seen him again. I wondered whether he now regretted his outburst: with Auguste it was hard to tell. By the time we returned to the house I had reluctantly accepted that I would have to be patient if I was to extract the whole story.

As it happened Auguste waylaid me next morning in the hall, apparently casually although something in his manner made me suspect that he had been waiting some time for me to appear.

'Today,' he said, clutching my arm, 'you and I are going up to the village. But we do not need to tell anyone.' He tapped the side of his nose and his straggling moustache seemed to stiffen with anticipation.

It was a bright, blustery morning; clouds chased each other like sailing ships over the sky, their shadows flying across the plain. Oncle Auguste took what seemed to me to be the most elaborate precautions to disguise our destination. He put on his battered gardening hat, collected his favourite rake from the stables, and instructed me to follow him with a wheel-barrow. As he shuffled along the front of the house, Lise smiled and nodded at us from the kitchen window. Looking up, I saw a curtain move in Tante Alice's bedroom: clearly Auguste knew what he was doing.

Once round the curve of the drive, the house out of sight, Auguste's back seemed to straighten and his step became firmer. The rake and wheelbarrow were hidden behind a bush, from where he retrieved a stout walking-stick. We crossed the road and began the long climb up the red brick path in the direction of the village walls. I would never have thought Auguste capable of the exertion required by this ascent but despite heavy breathing and occasional pauses he pressed on. Halfway up the hillside we reached a bench and sat for a moment to recover our strength. Oncle Auguste blew his nose vigorously into a large red handkerchief which he then care-fully inspected. Below we could see the grey slate roof of the house, and the plain stretching out beyond. The swaying trees almost concealed the lake at our feet, but I noticed the little rowing-boat bobbing about and tugging at its moorings. I was not, however, given much time to contemplate the view. Having rapidly found his breath for the final assault, Auguste pointed upwards and we set off again.

The last hundred yards were the steepest, but we reached the arch in the wall without further pause, and headed purposefully along the main street and into the square.

Occasionally lifting his hat to acknowledge a greeting, Auguste crossed the square and, pushing at a swing door with his stick, entered a small café opposite the church. This was the principal, indeed as it turned out, the only objective of our expedition. We sat down at a table in the window from where we could observe the whole square, and the proprietor materialised silently beside us.

'The usual, Monsieur Auguste?' he enquired. Auguste nodded. 'And one for the young man as well. Never mind the rules: I was his age when I had my first absinthe.' He turned to me. 'Now one is only allowed *anis*; the government interferes with everything,' he added mournfully.

A waiter appeared with two glasses of green liquid and a jug of water. Auguste added the water and the mixture turned cloudy. Despite his disparaging comment he took an appreciative, if noisy, first sip, then wiped his moustache with his handkerchief.

'Women, and especially my wife,' he said reflectively, 'fail to understand the need for these moments of peace in the day. But why worry them? Alice likes me to work in the garden so I am happy to satisfy her. If the eye does not see . . .'

It was quiet in the café. At that mid-morning hour we were the only customers. The pin-ball machine was deserted, the juke-box stood silent. A clock ticked loudly on the dark, mahogany wall, where the only decoration was a faded photograph of the village church. A notice by the glass swing door listed twenty regulations in small print under a forbidding heading in black letters: '*Repression de l'Ivresse Publique et Protection des Mineurs*'. Oncle Auguste sighed, whether from contentment or melancholy I could not tell.

'At your age,' he said again, 'I had a gun and a girl.' He paused to digest the thought; time telescoped. 'Then the war came. After the Marne we were at Verdun – the worst battle I ever knew. We held the Boches off in the end, but what a sacrifice.' He took off his glasses and rubbed his watery eyes. At this, as if obeying some signal, the waiter reappeared with a second glass of *anis* and more water.

Oncle Auguste fell silent while he began more rapidly to gulp down his drink. Then he stiffened, and looked alertly through the window. His eye had been caught by a black Mercedes which had halted at the far end of the square. A stout blonde woman and an older man emerged from the car and looked round them uncertainly. Auguste crouched forward, like a cat which has caught sight of mice at play. His tongue flickered along the bottom of his moustache.

'Germans,' he hissed, 'you can always tell them.' He became increasingly agitated, and his hands began to tremble. 'They came in '14, they came back in '40, and still they come. But we will always throw them out until they learn not to interfere.' Now he was muttering to himself, apparently in the grip of a strong emotion. I was alarmed by his sudden change of mood, but even so, unprepared for what followed.

Auguste pushed back his chair, reached for his hat, grabbed his walking-stick and moved to the door. Here he paused and looked sharply at his unsuspecting prey who were moving slowly up the opposite pavement, halting to peer into the shop windows.

'Forward!' cried Auguste suddenly. He flung open the door and began to shuffle rapidly over the deserted square. Half-way across he raised his stick: aiming it before him with both hands he broke into a shambling run. His hat flew off. '*Vive la France!*' he shouted. 'Ra-ta-ta-ta, ra-ta-ta-ta!'

The two Germans stood transfixed as Auguste approached at some speed: although he was running straight at them, they seemed incapable of movement. But a few yards before he reached his target, his solitary charge came to an end. He tripped and fell violently. As he lay motionless, his stick rolled slowly away from him.

I raced across the square to him as two men emerged from a shop and bent over his inert figure; he was badly winded and had lost his glasses, but appeared otherwise unharmed. They carried him to the pavement and sat him against the shop wall. Another man collected the hat and stick. Auguste opened his eyes, but said nothing.

A small crowd was gathering, but they stood back, watching us silently. I knelt beside Auguste.

'Don't worry, I have to leave you for a moment, then we'll go home,' I said quietly in his ear. He looked straight ahead and appeared not to hear me.

I trotted back to the café where the owner and the waiter were calmly observing the scene from the doorway. I was led to a telephone behind the bar where I turned a handle and requested the number of the house. After much whirring and clicking I heard a ringing tone and waited impatiently for a reply. It was a long time coming, but to my relief it was finally

Tante Alice who responded; the line echoed badly and she sounded a long way off.

'Tante Alice,' I shouted, 'I am in the village with Oncle Auguste. He has fallen over. Please can you send the car for us?' My voice rose as I spoke and for the first time I felt a moment of panic.

'In the village?' Tante Alice sounded irritated rather than alarmed. 'What is he doing there? He should be in the garden.'

'I will explain later. But can someone fetch us quickly?'

'The car has gone out,' said Tante Alice, as if it had driven itself away. 'You must go to the Citroën garage and ask them to bring you down. But don't let them overcharge us.' With that, she rang off.

When I returned across the square I found that the transport problem was being solved in an unexpected manner. The elderly German who, when I left, had been hovering uneasily on the edge of the crowd standing round Oncle Auguste, had come forward and offered his Mercedes. Taking the lack of any coherent response for acceptance, he had fetched his car and driven it close to Auguste, who was now being slowly helped into the back. I thought he might resist help from such an unwelcome quarter but he still seemed scarcely aware of his surroundings. Passively he allowed himself to be propped against the back seat, stick in hand. I too climbed into the back and from there guided our hosts through the village and down the hill to the house.

Neither husband nor wife spoke during our short journey: whether it was embarrassment, politeness, or lack of language which inhibited them, they sought no explanation for Auguste's conduct nor did I volunteer any. Silently we turned in at the gates and slipped along the drive to the front steps, where Tante Alice stood impatiently waiting for us. She quickly opened the car door and without a word of acknowledgement or thanks to Auguste's rescuers began to hustle him into the house. As he reached the top step he turned and for the first time caught my eye. For a moment I thought he winked.

It was left to me to convey a mixture of apology and gratitude to our rescuers who had remained seated in the car. As I did so the man reached into his pocket and handed me Auguste's spectacles: one of the lenses had cracked. He leaned out of the window and glanced thoughtfully up at the house while his wife looked stolidly ahead of her. Then he turned the car round, and it disappeared slowly down the drive.

For a couple of days Auguste did not appear downstairs; meals were taken to him on a tray. Whether he was genuinely incapacitated or was being punished by Tante Alice for his escapade was not clear to me. Madeleine thought it was the latter but she was sure, she said, that Auguste was keeping up his spirits by sleeping wrapped in the *Tricolore,* as he liked to do, it seemed, in times of stress.

The episode was not, however, a subject of conversation; the aunts simply closed over it like the waves of the sea. Only Tante Yvonne was curious to know precisely what had happened in the village that morning, although she did not show undue surprise when I told her privately of Auguste's unexpected assault. She implied that some rather similar incident had taken place many years previously.

'I am afraid my brother never fully recovered from the First War,' she remarked. 'All those guns blasting off blew away some of his wits. They made him an army quartermaster after the Armistice but he could never keep his supplies in order. Everyone was thankful when in the end he resigned his commission.'

For my part, I was burning to ask Tante Yvonne about my grandfather Jack, but could think of no way of introducing the subject. I was afraid of upsetting her by recounting what Auguste had told me. She had not mentioned his name to me since my arrival and this led me to suppose that the subject must still be sensitive for her. Only a few days later, however, I noticed that Auguste, now up and about, was staring at me fixedly from the other side of the dinner table. I looked away, but felt his gaze still pointed in my direction.

As the plates were cleared away he leaned over the table and splashed some more wine into his glass.

'Yvonne, if you ask me the boy's going to be like Jack,' he suddenly addressed his sister sitting opposite.

I remained silent, my eyes on the polished mahogany, quite unable to look up at Tante Yvonne beside me. Then I felt her hand on my chin as she turned my face towards her. Her hooded eyes gave me her by now familiar appraising look as she chuckled.

'You are right, Auguste. He has Jack's nose and mouth. But the child doesn't know what we are talking about.'

'I do indeed, Tante Yvonne. Oncle Auguste has told me.' I found my voice at last.

She looked reproachfully at her brother who was struggling to rise from his chair. 'That was unwise, Auguste. If his parents have said nothing, it is perhaps for good reason.'

'Nonsense, Yvonne, nonsense. The boy belongs here now . . .' He did not finish this thought, but Tante Yvonne rose in her turn and leaning on my shoulder took me to a cupboard by the fireplace.

'There is an album on the top shelf,' she said. 'Let us bring it over to the light and I will show you your grandfather Jack as I knew him.'

I reached up for the heavy cloth-bound volume and carried it over to the table. Tante Yvonne sat down again, and opened the dark pages which were covered with yellowing, sepia photographs. Some had come unstuck and lay in the fold of the book; while the writing was by now mostly illegible.

A page was turned and her finger paused. There, looking up at me, was a young man in uniform, smart in his Sam Browne and khaki breeches, with clear, rather staring eyes – possibly the effect of the camera – smooth dark hair, and a neatly trimmed moustache. It was unmistakably my grandfather, although he appeared younger than in any picture I had seen of him at home. Again she turned the page. Jack was standing on the steps of the house, still wearing uniform but relaxed and smiling, a girl in a long dress with a dark sash round her waist on his arm. With a mischievous smile she was looking up at him to say something, possibly a jibe at the expense of the unseen photographer on the terrace below them. Despite the great lapse of years, I knew Yvonne at once; there was the same self-assurance in her bearing and something in the glance, too, which had not changed. More pictures followed: Jack and Yvonne together on horseback, a picnic by the lake with a crowd of officers and other girls whom I could not identify, and two youthful figures standing a little stiffly with two boys between them: Lise and Auguste I recognised, while the boys, Yvonne told me, were Henri and Antoine. I wanted to see more, but abruptly Tante Yvonne closed the book.

'Not all memories are happy ones,' she sighed. 'Naturally I was upset when he told me of his engagement. Perhaps I was wrong to expect him to wait so long. But I could not abandon my brothers at that age, any more than he could give up his career.'

She paused, her hand resting on the album. We were alone now, but through the double doors which led into the drawing-room I could see that a game of bridge was in preparation. Lots were being drawn for partners while Bob, his head wreathed in the smoke of one of his favourite pipes, was arranging four chairs round the card table. The door on to the terrace was open and Tante Yvonne, always suspicious of the night air, asked me to close it.

'You know,' she looked at me defiantly as I came back to the table, 'I could have chosen from a hundred other suitors! He was so very English, your grandfather, with a true English-man's sense of honour: he wrote to say that he knew he had let me down, and I replied telling him not to be stupid. But what truly grieved me was his conviction that after his marriage he could not return here.' For the first time she looked indignant.

'People and places are the most precious things in life, and you do not cast them aside like old clothes.'

She turned towards me and put a hand on my arm. 'Now I'll tell you something I never mentioned to your father when he visited me – it seemed wrong somehow to stir up the past with him. But it's this: although I never saw Jack again, my brother Henri did meet him once just before Jack was killed on the Somme. One night Henri was called out of the line to escort an English colonel to the local headquarters. As they talked, Jack discovered who Henri was and after that he insisted that Henri stay with him the whole of the next day. He wanted to know everything that had happened to us here in the intervening years: Henri told me that it was as if he could never hear enough. When they finally separated he promised Henri that he would come back and see us after the war. Then only a few days later he was hit, and the chance for us to meet again was lost. I found out much later that he had died in the same week as my brother, Antoine. Florence has been urging me to tell you all this: she did not feel she should do so herself.'

There was another silence. 'I am sorry you never knew your grandfather,' Yvonne said at length. 'He was a very charming, amusing man: I so much wanted to see him once more. But life's paths are mysterious: I can after all now find him again in you. My old brother is not always completely wrong!'

She sat back and looked me up and down with a gentle smile. Then she rose and shuffled slowly down the long table, moving heavily from chair to chair as she passed behind the bridge players and back to her corner seat in the drawing-room.

## IV  Tante Alice

Most people were a little afraid of Tante Alice. Old age had not been kind to her appearance: her receding white hair piled high on her head, her wrinkled leathery skin and her skeletal countenance gave one the impression of confronting a gargoyle – it was easy to imagine her face staring down at you from the end of a church roof. But it was the eyes which gave her a more sinister aspect; sunken and expressionless, they resembled a snake's eyes and glittered during her not infrequent moments of irritation or anger.

Although reportedly very wealthy in her own right – no one was sure to what extent – Tante Alice was known in the family to be so parsimonious as virtually to constitute a female incarnation of Harpagon, Molière's celebrated miser. Stories of her meanness were passed from hand to hand, and gave Tante Yvonne much quiet amusement at the expense of her sister-in-law. One evening Tante Yvonne showed me with a little smile an envelope which she treasured, having received it some months previously by post from Alice: it had been carefully unglued, turned inside out and readdressed! Less entertaining was Tante Alice's habit of moving repeatedly round the house in the evening extinguishing every electric light bulb so that we were condemned to live in an encircling gloom relieved only by small pools of light where we sat. If Tante Alice indulged herself she did so in secret, or through what she fondly imagined was successful deception, such as the neat whisky which, screwing up her face, she drank before lunch each day from a large patent medicine bottle that she kept in a cupboard in the dining-room.

Alice came from a family of rich, socially ambitious silk manufacturers in Lyons. It was something of a mystery that she should have married Auguste, then an impecunious artillery officer stationed in the centre of France. But from the day of her marriage she had taken charge of her patient husband who had only once, during the First War, managed to escape from her suffocating embrace. Auguste's passivity and lack of enterprise were the counterpart of his wife's restless energy and may indeed over the years have become the product of it. He and Alice retained a small apartment in Lyons but Auguste preferred to spend the greater part of the year in the north with his family. They had no children, whether by accident or design I did not know. Certainly I have met few women who appeared less maternal than Alice.

Tante Alice owned a number of farms near Lyons as well as two or three in the north, behind Boulogne. An only child, she had inherited these from her father. In the autumn of every year she would visit her properties in the south, spending several days as the self-invited guest of each farmer during which time she would carefully examine the state of the buildings and the level of the husbandry. Her tenants were known to look forward to this progress with foreboding but they no doubt felt it prudent to show hospitality to their proprietress. The farms in the north escaped more lightly as, with the assistance of Joseph in the Citroën, Alice was able to confine her visits to a single day's expedition.

She usually preferred to make her inspections alone. One evening, however, she surprised me by suggesting that I accompany her the next day to see 'my little farmer behind Boulogne', on the grounds that a change of air from time to time did everyone good. As we sat in the back of the car the next morning, behind an unusually good-humoured Joseph who was visibly enjoying the excursion, I noticed that Tante Alice had dressed with care and that she had added even more rings than usual to her long fingers, so that her hands, which were like the claws of some large bird, literally shone with diamonds. She held a capacious black handbag in her lap from which, once we were under way, she drew a notebook and, with an old pencil, began to check columns of figures, marking the bottom of each with a little tick.

While she was absorbed in this task, I gazed through the car windows at the passing scene. Now that we had left the Flemish plain, the countryside was changing. The flat fields gave way to undulating hills, some entirely under the plough, others, given over to pasture, looking as green and smooth as billiard tables. These in turn were succeeded by woods through which we drove along twisting roads, until we came out on to a large expanse of farmland devoted mainly to wheat fields, with the sea in the distance.

We were nearing our destination. Tante Alice snapped her notebook away in her bag and, leaning forward, gave some clearly unnecessary instruction to Joseph who scarcely bothered to acknowledge it. Turning off the road, the car rattled down an unmade drive and into a large courtyard with a long, low, whitewashed farmhouse at the end, and barns and stables on each side. As we came to a halt, we could hear dogs barking from all directions until a door opened to reveal a burly man who stood quietly observing us while Joseph helped Tante Alice out of the car. The farmer's bulky, powerful frame seemed to have been crammed with difficulty into his black Sunday suit. With somewhat forced geniality he came forward, shook us by the hand, introducing himself to me as Henri Martin, and led us into a room with wooden beams and a highly polished tiled floor. Here we were greeted by the farmer's wife, a small bird-like woman who darted round us arranging chairs and setting out glasses with fluttering movements as if she was trying to find some way out of the confined space.

As the customary bottle of *porto* was brought out of a corner cupboard, the door was pushed open and a small boy of about my own age appeared on the threshold. He had a narrow, pinched face but eyes which were so large that they seemed almost out of proportion to his other features. He too had clearly been dressed for the occasion and his hair slicked down with water, so that I suddenly felt conscious of my khaki shirt and darned, woollen jersey.

The boy came forward and shook hands with studied politeness. Then his mother intervened, suggesting that her son should show me round the farm while she and her husband had a talk before lunch with Tante Alice. Obediently he led me out of the room, down a dark passage and into a walled garden at the back of the house, which was all the more attractive for being unexpected. A large expanse of grass was neatly cut, roses and wisteria climbed the stone walls, and a flower-bed down one side had been carefully tended.

For a moment neither of us spoke, until the boy asked abruptly, 'Is she really your aunt?'

'No, not really,' I replied hesitantly.

'That's all right, then.' He seemed relieved. 'Come and see the horses.'

With evident pleasure he kicked off his neatly polished shoes and, barefoot, led the way over the grass, through a gate and into a field where two large carthorses were standing, nose to tail, under a chestnut tree. We went up to stroke them.

'This is Giant,' he said, burying his head in the side of one of the horses, and adding without a pause, 'did Madame Alice tell you that we may have to leave here soon?'

'No,' I said indifferently. 'Why do you want to go?'

'We don't want to go at all.' He lifted his head and looked at me indignantly. 'We have always lived here. But my father has problems with money. That's what he is talking about with Madame Alice. He said he hoped that she would understand, but he did not think she would. Perhaps you can help with her?' This last remark was uttered more despondently than hopefully.

We left the horses and made our way round the farm buildings. These, I noticed, were well kept but seemed strangely empty: there were none of the customary impedimenta of old and new farm machinery, no tractors, no fodder for livestock.

Then we returned to the garden and stood there rather awkwardly. The boy's obvious depression inhibited conversation, and the usual questions about school and holidays seemed somehow out of place. He sat down on the step and was carefully lacing up his shoes when we were called in to lunch. The atmosphere was visibly strained: Martin and his wife looked downcast, while Tante Alice appeared irritated but determined to maintain a flow of conversation about every subject except the one which was evidently on the minds of our three hosts. Madame Martin served a huge meal: pâtés, salads, a great side of roast beef, several cheeses and a much decorated ice-cream cake – the courses seemed never-ending – but even when complimenting her hostess

Tante Alice appeared to do so in a barbed way.

'An excellent lunch, Madame, I am so glad that despite your problems you can provide so well for your family.'

At this Monsieur Martin clearly could not contain himself further. 'We shall always look after our guests properly as long as we are in this house, Madame,' he said sharply, 'and we are now in your hands as to how long that will be. I will not repeat what I said earlier in the other room. We can only ask you to reflect seriously on what we have proposed as our whole future is at stake.'

This little speech, uttered with great dignity, only served to make Tante Alice more irritable. Glancing at the boy and myself she suggested tartly that it was perhaps not appropriate to pursue the subject in our presence. But the farmer was not to be diverted.

'On the contrary, Madame, my son is fully aware of the situation. His future as well as ours is concerned. Is that not so, Pierre?' The boy nodded solemnly.

Alice became agitated. 'I have said that I will think about it, but I can promise nothing,' she said, adding sourly, 'my resources are not unlimited and I have many responsibilities.'

Tante Alice made an early move to leave. No sooner, however, were we in the car and driving back to the road than she exploded with anger, talking as much to herself as to me and ignoring Joseph who could hear and would no doubt later relay to Zoë every word.

'There is no limit to the demands of these people! For two years they have paid no rent and now they ask me for a loan.

Why should I pour more money down their throats? If they cannot make the farm pay they should leave and we will find someone more capable. Why do I need their paper?' This last remark being a reference to a closely written document which Martin had handed to Alice as she took leave of him.

She began to scrutinise Martin's notes, but continued to give vent to muttered exclamations of 'incredible' and 'preposterous' whenever her temper got the better of her, like the explosions of an erupting volcano. Then as we neared our village, she leaned across the seat and gripped my arm with a bony hand.

'You will of course observe discretion about what you have heard this afternoon,' she said with a smile which somehow failed to reach her eyes. 'Questions of money are always . . .' she paused for emphasis . . . 'most delicate. No one in the family, not even Yvonne, appreciates the burdens I carry, and have to carry alone.'

I tried to escape her glance by staring at the back of Joseph's wrinkled neck. It occurred to me that Tante Alice was already regretting having made me an involuntary witness of the way she conducted her affairs. Then I thought of Pierre Martin, of how he had buried his head in the horse's side, and of his appeal to me to help. I knew I must say something to Tante Yvonne, even if this meant incurring the old lady's wrath.

Fortunately, Tante Yvonne made it easy for me. At dinner Alice, who was normally loquacious about any journey she had made, proved strangely evasive over her visit to the Martins. Afterwards she seized Auguste by the arm and announced that she was retiring early to bed. No sooner had she gone than Yvonne beckoned me to a chair at one end of the dining-room.

'Now,' she said quietly, 'tell me what really happened today. I like Henri Martin: he is solid and honest and they are a good family.'

After some hesitation and mentioning Alice's enjoinder to keep silent, I told Tante Yvonne everything I had seen and heard. As I spoke she began to look fierce, and then exclaimed, 'Of course they must be helped. Our family would never be forgiven, and rightly, if the Martins were forced out of a farm which they have worked for generations. The question is how to persuade Alice. Only she has the means, and they are ample, to do what is right. We must find a way of convincing her. But I must wait for her to speak to me, which, in her own time, she will do.'

Tante Alice kept matters to herself for several days. She was more than usually irritable, muttering to herself and snapping at Auguste who was in one of his 'tired' periods. Yvonne waited patiently for her sister-in-law, knowing that in the end she would want to confide in her. When one evening Alice, with a heavy sigh, said, 'Yvonne, I must tell you about my impossible farmer,' Yvonne was ready.

As they both looked through Henri Martin's accounts, Yvonne said, 'My dear Alice, the situation is easily soluble if you have faith in the Martins, as I do. You know as well as I that his farm has needed the right equipment for years. Buy him the tools and he will do the work.'

'But . . .'

'No buts! Indeed, I have a proposal to make to you. I will lend the money myself to Henri Martin. I regard him as an excellent investment. I feel sure that he and I could reach an arrangement. I trust you would have no objection?'

Tante Alice looked first amazed, then indignant. 'Out of the question, Yvonne! It would be most improper. He is my tenant.'

'It would be even more improper for Martin to have to give up his farm. The choice is yours, of course, but help he must have.'

As Tante Alice left the room grumbling to herself, Tante Yvonne turned to me with a wry smile.

'I am glad that she did not ask me where I would find such a sum. But if there is one thing Alice hates more than spending money, it is interference in her affairs. She will of course make the loan, and I will send a little message to the Martins to wish them well with their new start. Now, where is Lise with my tisane?'

*V François*

Zoë talked a great deal to herself. She was always muttering as she shuffled around in her kitchen, a habit perhaps acquired through being unable to communicate with Lise, who spent so many hours there. You soon knew from the flow of irritable comment if Zoë had received some unwelcome instructions although she was quite used to having her objections disregarded. Occasionally she complained more loudly to her niece Julienne who did the cleaning and ironing, but it would be wrong to suppose that she was habitually bad-tempered. She enjoyed company, and I would often sit at the long kitchen table, dipping a spoon into a sauce or cake mixture while I listened to her gossip in her guttural northern accent. Zoë and Julienne reserved for more emotional or conspiratorial exchanges their incomprehensible Flemish *patois,* which was as local as the beer or the old windmill standing above the village.

One of Zoë's favourite moments in the day was the arrival of old Jacques the postman, who still collected and delivered letters by bicycle. His son, young Jacques, worked at the local garage and had offered him various forms of motorised transport, but he had rejected them all. He usually reached the house at the end of his round, signalling his arrival by ringing a large cow-bell which stood on a table in the hall and was used otherwise for summoning us to meals precisely ten minutes after Lise had tolled the bell on the roof. He then liked to repair to the kitchen for a drink with Zoë; I would hear the two of them commiserating with each other over their respective employers or about life in general, while Jacques downed a *coup de rouge* before pushing his bicycle back up the long hill.

One morning I found Tante Yvonne reading a note, just delivered, whose excessively large, sloping handwriting seemed itself to be part of its message.

'This lady wants to rent the white cottage for a year,' she said. 'I cannot think why: she will find everything very simple and quiet here after Paris.'

She handed me the letter, from which a powerful, sweet scent emanated. It read:

Mademoiselle,
May I introduce myself as a friend of Madame de

Montigny who knows you well and tells me that you have on your property a small house which you might be willing to let to me for some twelve months. Having recently lost my husband I need to be quiet and would be most grateful if you could consider my request. I shall be visiting friends in the north in a week's time and, if I may, will take the opportunity to call on you.

Respectful greetings,

Hortense Duvalier

'Well now,' said Tante Yvonne thoughtfully, 'I haven't seen Hélène de Montigny for several years. How does she know the white cottage is empty, I wonder? Let us await this fragrant lady.'

We did not have to wait long. A few days later, as the aunts were drinking coffee after lunch, Zoë showed in a tiny well-dressed, plumpish woman in her early thirties, with blonde curls and a dimpled chin. She looked enquiringly round with an engaging smile.

'It is so kind of you to receive me,' she began once the introductions had been made. 'Hélène de Montigny has told me so much about you all.'

'That was kind of Hélène,' said Tante Yvonne, 'but as she must have told you, we have alas only corresponded occasionally over the past few years. How is she these days?'

'Well, I think, well . . .' Madame Duvalier seemed a little confused by this simple question, and quickly moved on. 'I hope you did not mind my enquiry, but since my bereavement

I have been looking for an escape from Paris for a while.'

'And your husband?' enquired Tante Alice, giving her a beady glance.

'He was a lawyer, Madame. He died suddenly only three months ago: it was a great shock to me.' She took out a handkerchief, and I recognised the scent.

'You will find the little house very simple,' said Yvonne, 'but we keep it well furnished and equipped, and if it suits you, you are of course welcome to use it. My niece Madeleine will show you round.'

After Madame Duvalier had left the room, Tante Alice observed, 'That woman is not telling the truth; you should be careful, Yvonne.'

'I will of course write to Hélène,' said Tante Yvonne, 'but the lady seems presentable, the cottage is empty and I see no reason to refuse it to her if she wants it. We shall see.'

Within half an hour Madeleine was back with an enthusiastic Madame Duvalier. 'It is just what I need, and so charming,' she exclaimed, her little curls bobbing. 'I will, if I may, move in next week. This may seem a little soon to you, Mademoiselle, but I cannot bear to remain in Paris one day longer.'

Tante Yvonne looked pensive once Madame Duvalier had left. 'She is either rich, or light-headed, or both,' she remarked. 'Do you know, she never enquired about the rent? You are right, Alice, there is something a little strange about this lady.'

It was, I think, the next day that a telegram from Florence's younger son, François, arrived, announcing that he was coming to stay. Florence appeared pleased but was clearly surprised at this unexpected news. François and his Belgian wife came rarely to the house, confining their visits to grand occasions such as weddings or funerals and preferring if they left Paris to head south. He worked for an American company, but exactly in what capacity was obscure. His way of life was a little mysterious and, from the way Tante Yvonne occasionally spoke of him, not always irreproachable. The fact that he lived in Paris, had Parisian friends and had almost entirely escaped the family network also made him something of an outsider.

François arrived a week or so after Madame Duvalier had moved into the cottage. One evening, as I returned from a fishing expedition at the lake, I saw Florence walking slowly round the lawn on the arm of a tall, very thin man whose languid air made you feel that his attire could appropriately have included a cane and straw boater. As it was, he was clad, somewhat pretentiously I thought, in a tweed jacket and matching plus-fours, no doubt in deference to his excursion to the country. When I approached I saw that he had a pencil moustache and very soft, almost frightened brown eyes which belied his self-assured, faintly supercilious manner.

'Still carp in the lake, I see.' He peered, as if short-sighted, at my catch. 'I don't think I could stand another one after all those we ate during the War. When did something new last happen here, I wonder?' he added, smiling knowingly at his mother.

'Well, for a start, we have a new tenant in the white cottage,' replied Florence, looking sideways at François. 'She is Hortense Duvalier and a Parisian. Maybe you know her?'

'Really, mother, Paris is a large city.' He dismissed the suggestion somewhat abruptly, I thought.

'No matter, she is coming to see us tomorrow so you can find out for yourself,' remarked Florence equably.

He made no further comment, nor did he react when Tante Yvonne reminded everyone at dinner that Madame Duvalier was coming to tea the next afternoon. Later, however, François took me to one side.

'I have a small favour to ask you,' he said, his glance darting uneasily over my shoulder. 'It is just possible that Madame Duvalier and I may have met somewhere in Paris. I would not wish her to be startled by finding me so unexpectedly here. Perhaps, tomorrow morning, you would be kind enough to give her this little note.' And he whisked a small blue envelope from his waistcoat pocket, thrusting it furtively into my hand.

The white cottage was at the far end of the property, with an entrance on to the road. It was a little house built in fact of the local red brick, but taking its name from the door and shutters which were traditionally painted white. When I knocked the next morning there was no answer, but I followed the sound of a small dog barking in the garden at the rear to find Hortense Duvalier seated at a round table on the grass, drinking coffee. Mardi blundered excitedly through the hedge behind me, although she declined to take an interest in the black poodle that was lying under the table, and retired to a suitable distance. The sun had already reached the garden through a clump of copper beeches beyond the hedge, but

Hortense pulled her quilted dressing-gown round her shoulders as if she found the air still cold.

She did not appear surprised by my errand. Taking the note with a smile, she read it through quickly, and folded it in her hand. The smile gave way to a thoughtful expression while her eyes seemed focused on the middle distance.

'Poor François,' she said, looking in the direction of the house. 'I do not think he is very happy. Now come and sit down and have some coffee, and tell me more about the family.'

She patted the bench beside her and began to question me about Tante Yvonne, Florence and what I knew of François' brother and sister. She was, I thought, rather like a china doll with her round, open face and flaxen curls, and plump little hands. She smiled and laughed readily and within a few minutes I felt much at ease, telling stories about the house which she followed intently.

Eventually she said, 'Now I feel I know everyone better: this afternoon will be less of an ordeal. Can we be friends, you and I?' She bent over and kissed my cheek, then went indoors.

At five o'clock the whole family was for once assembled on the terrace – even Oncle Auguste had drifted in from the garden – as Hortense came up through the meadow and across the lawn. She wore a pink dress and straw hat and walked with quick little steps. All eyes followed her progress over the grass: only François, hovering uneasily behind the circle of chairs, affected less than an intense interest. He shook hands with Hortense coolly and then took a seat at some distance from her while Florence plied her with questions about Paris. Tea and a plate of Zoë's rather heavy *tartines* were handed round, while François still said nothing. Indeed, he seemed increasingly restless and morose.

Finally, however, Hortense moved to leave, and he too stood up. Turning to her he said gravely, 'Madame, perhaps you will allow me to escort you back to the cottage.'

In an equally serious tone of voice, but with, I thought, an amused glance at us all, she replied, 'That is most considerate of you, Monsieur.'

During the first days of the ensuing week François made one or two carefully announced calls on Madame Duvalier, but after a short while he began to spend the greater part of each day at the cottage, reappearing only at mealtimes when he sat in awkward silence next to his mother. Tante Alice declared indignantly that she had observed François and Hortense walking arm in arm by the lake. Supposing they were seen 'by the village'? she enquired rhetorically. The dilemma of Florence and Tante Yvonne was particularly painful: I often came across them engaged in quiet if unhappy conversation. The two old ladies were plainly at a loss and each was inclined to look to the other to resolve the situation. Yvonne believed that Florence should speak to her son, while Florence, reasoning that Hortense was Yvonne's tenant, thought that Yvonne could most conveniently terminate the arrangement. Madeleine, meanwhile, ostentatiously steered clear of her brother's affairs, behaving rather unconvincingly as if nothing was amiss.

One afternoon, as I was walking up the meadow, I heard

voices on the other side of the hedge. Peeping over, I saw François and Hortense sitting on the bench in the cottage garden, holding hands and laughing. Hortense caught sight of me at once and called me in. François seemed a different person, relaxed and self-confident: even his eyes had lost their usual apprehensive expression.

It was already late afternoon. A little wind from the plain swirled round us, rustling the trees. As François went indoors to fetch another cushion, Hortense gave me a serious look and I sensed a question in her mind. But she chose not to address it, remarking instead on the beauty of the evening in an over-casual voice; and when François returned she and he continued to gossip about a mutual friend in Paris. I left them absorbed in each other, enjoying a country idyll that could not, I sensed, last much longer.

Nor did it. As we were seated at lunch only a day later, Zoë appeared in the dining-room. Instead of approaching Tante Yvonne she chose, with a characteristic sense of theatre, to make her announcement from the door.

'Madame François has just rung from the station and is asking for the car,' she declared with a toothless smirk.

François looked first incredulous, then alarmed and finally distraught. In slow motion he rose from his chair and left the room in search of Joseph and the car. Tante Alice tittered, while Yvonne and Florence glanced inscrutably at each other from opposite sides of the table. If Florence had taken the initiative in proposing to Chantal that she come to collect her straying husband, the idea had, I felt sure, been Tante Yvonne's.

Florence was not fond of her daughter-in-law and when she arrived half an hour later I could see why. Small and dark, she moved without apparent pleasure round the lunch table, pecking briefly at each proffered cheek before settling down at one end with a sandwich and a cup of coffee brought in by Zoë. I wondered how she had explained her sudden arrival to François. Had she said bluntly that she had been summoned to stop him making a fool of himself in front of his family, or was her presence in itself enough to make the point?

As we were all leaving the dining-room, François cornered me in the hall, just as he had on the evening of his arrival. He made no effort to disguise his unhappiness.

'Can you please go to Hortense and explain?' he pleaded. 'Say I will come and see her later when I can.' He swallowed convulsively and moved quickly to join his wife who had already vanished upstairs. Without pausing I slipped through the kitchen and ran down to the cottage, coming in through the garden where I found Hortense arranging some flowers at a table. She listened quietly to my news and then, sitting down rather heavily, remained silent for a full minute.

'So,' she said at last, 'we must pay for our indiscretion. I told François he should come here only occasionally. He wanted to see me settled here, but then he could not stay away: that too was my fault. We have enjoyed each other's company too much. The family is quite right of course: this could not continue. Would you please tell Mademoiselle Yvonne that I shall be returning to Paris as soon as possible. I should like her to know that today, before François tries to make me change my

76

mind. She will understand, and I hope she will believe that I meant no harm to anyone. Perhaps you would take her these flowers.' She returned to the table and picked up the arrangement of wild flowers she had been making.

When I reached the house I found Tante Yvonne and Tante Florence seated on the terrace winding balls of wool. I gave Tante Yvonne Hortense's message and handed her the flowers, which she laid gently beside her on the table. If she was relieved by what I said she did not show it; Florence, however, smiled happily.

'François has spent most of his married life getting into trouble,' she murmured, 'and the rest of us have devoted time and effort during the past six years rescuing him from his stupidity. This infatuation will pass like all the others. If only he was happier at home . . .' and she glanced up at the window of his room.

Two days later, François and Chantal left for Paris. I do not know whether he saw Hortense again before he left: I rather think not. But as he stood by himself in the hall, waiting for his wife to come downstairs and for Joseph to bring up the car, he put his hand in the pocket of his unbuttoned overcoat and shyly produced a small parcel which he slipped into my hand.

'This is for you,' he said with a mournful smile, 'we found it in the village last week. She thought you should have it.'

Later, when I unwrapped the gift in my room, I found it was an old, painted china cup. Round the outside various mythological figures joined hands in a dance, led by Hermes, the messenger of the gods.

## VI  *Tante Thérèse*

Tante Thérèse was so quiet and self-effacing that you often forgot she was in the room. She was the youngest of the three sisters and, since the death some ten years previously of her husband, a local academic at Tours, her life had fallen into an unvarying pattern: the winters spent on the Loire in the little house which she now shared with her companion, Mathilde, while in the spring she would travel north to pass the summer months with her sisters. Her two daughters, both married, had husbands who seemingly preferred the Loire to Flanders, but they and Thérèse appeared content with an arrangement whereby their numerous offspring were consigned to her care during the long summer vacations; while the children, notion-ally supervised by a shifting populace of nannies, made the most of their freedom in the property.

Thérèse was small and neat; although in her early seventies, she was still good-looking with a round, soft face and very dark, almost black eyes. Her attractiveness was increased by an indefinable but perceptible air of vulnerability: when she smiled or spoke it was to invite your protection or support. The contrast with Mathilde – talkative, assertive and always a little too formally dressed for the country – was striking, yet for years the two had been inseparable. While Thérèse sat in a corner quietly sewing or reading, Mathilde, her hands and her elbows working, held forth on behalf of both of them. Almost daily Thérèse would move to the piano and play the same pieces by Bach or Chopin which she had evidently learnt many years previously. Despite the thin tone of the instru-ment, I loved to hear her play and the music she chose became for me indissociable from the daily round of the house.

While Tante Yvonne felt protective towards Thérèse she could not resist gently mocking her placid nature. 'Love never raged like a forest fire within my sister,' she once said to me, 'the undergrowth is perhaps a little damp.'

This last remark was accompanied by a sardonic glance at a framed photograph of Thérèse as Tante Yvonne told me that 'the Professor' would shortly be arriving from Paris for his annual stay at the house. He was, she explained, an old friend of Thérèse's husband, who taught law at the Sorbonne and, although several years younger than Thérèse, he had long shown a discreet interest in his deceased friend's widow, which she had always tolerated rather than reciprocated. Tante Yvonne derived considerable amusement from this silent courtship.

There was quite a stir in the house on the morning of the professor's arrival and I noticed that the aunts came down rather more carefully dressed than usual. Thérèse put bunches of flowers in his room, and Florence disappeared into the kitchen to supervise the preparation of lunch. Joseph could be seen in the courtyard washing down the Citroën with a hose. He then drove the still gleaming-wet car down the drive to meet the connecting train from Paris – known as the 'omnibus' – which stopped at midday at the village station on the other side of the hill.

Half an hour later he returned. I was waiting on the stairs, no more than usually disturbed by the weak but identifiable stench, inadequately masked by scent, which, when it rose from the cesspit below the house, emanated from a privy concealed by a wallpapered door in the bend of the staircase. Through the windows I saw a short, thin man with a white goatee beard and an ascetic, angular face emerge from the back of the car. He sported an old-fashioned travelling cloak and on entering the hall he discarded it with a flourish worthy of an opera singer arriving on stage. As I descended the steps he swung round to greet me, hand extended.

'Aha, young man, we have not I think previously met? University Professor Léon Dufour. How agreeable it is to return to the cradle of this charming family. And how are the ladies?' Without waiting for a reply he swept into the drawing-room where voices were at once raised in greeting.

At lunch the professor, who was seated between Yvonne and Thérèse, ate sparingly but held forth almost without interruption. He moved effortlessly from complaining about the low calibre of his students to the state of the Fourth Republic and the condition of the world. The whole table was, for once, silenced as the professor imparted to us his views on the Parisian and then the global scene. That evening, taking his cue from my presence, he treated us to a disquisition on the differences between Anglo-Saxon law and the *Code Napoléon.* The coming week promised, I thought, to be something of an endurance test.

The professor habitually rose late in the morning and would then retire with a cup of coffee to the small library behind the salon where he would bury himself in *La Croix,* the only daily newspaper that the family received. Articles which he wished to read aloud later to Thérèse were ringed with a red pencil, much to the irritation of Tante Alice who usually liked to monopolise the paper herself. Some stories caught his eye because they demonstrated the parochialism of his fellow Frenchmen – a favourite theme. Others served as a pretext for him to dilate on the state of French politics or the law. The insidious plotting of the Freemasons whose activities were solely directed at undermining Church and State, appeared to be a particular obsession for which *La Croix* furnished ample material.

After lunch Léon would offer his arm to Thérèse and

suggest that she accompany him on a stroll to the lake, an invitation which she invariably accepted with a small show of reluctance but with evident pleasure. One afternoon Mathilde, whose offer to accompany them had been politely declined, returned to the drawing-room and anxiously eyed the couple as they slowly disappeared from the terrace down into the meadow. Tante Yvonne was also sitting in the window looking thoughtfully at their retreating figures. The room was quiet. Mathilde sighed.

'I have a feeling that this year he may ask her. I could not of course live with them.' She spoke almost to herself.

Yvonne grunted. 'He may ask but I doubt whether Thérèse will accept. She is a good listener of course, but there are, all the same, limits . . .' She gave me an amused glance, aware that I now fled the room whenever the professor was settling down to a lecture.

It was Tante Yvonne who the same day unwittingly pushed matters forward although she had, I suspect, the rather different intention of shaking the professor's garrulous self-confidence of which in truth not only I had become a little weary.

'My dear Léon,' she said at dinner, 'I am in need of the help of an eminent jurist such as yourself. I should be grateful for your arbitration in a territorial dispute which I have been unable to resolve. My two most ill-tempered tenants have reached deadlock but you I feel sure will be able to turn the key.'

The professor preened himself. 'There are few problems, Yvonne, which do not yield to the application of reason. If we could replace our politicians with men of intelligence and objectivity France would again find her destiny.'

'My problem concerns the cultivation of a single field, not the destinies of France,' rejoined Yvonne, 'but it appears to be no less intractable. Bommaert and André have now opened hostilities.'

'Hostilities? And what, dear lady, is the difficulty?'

Yvonne sighed. 'There is a pasture lying between their two farms which André has been using for his cattle. Bommaert maintains that it was previously farmed by his own grandfather and unjustly taken by the André family when his grandfather died in the Great War. He has always asserted this claim but, alas, my own papers do not show the circumstances under which the use of the land passed to the Andrés.

'Now they wish to plough up the pasture for crops and Bommaert has chosen to regard this as a provocation. The only access is through a right of way along one of his own fields which Bommaert has closed off until his claim is satisfied. The two families are on the point of exchanging blows, but neither can afford to go to court, nor should they. Only the lawyers would profit from that.'

The professor looked pensive. 'I feel sure we can devise a solution,' he said at length. 'But first we must of course examine the situation on the ground.' He eyed me at the end of the table. 'Young man, tomorrow you will lead me there.'

As it happened I knew the disputed field well. It backed on to a copse where the ground was mined with rabbit warrens. Only the previous week I had spent a happy afternoon with the two Bommaert sons, the one armed with a shotgun, the other with a ferret in a sack. You put the ferret down a rabbit hole and waited breathlessly to see which of the hundreds of possible exits the fleeing rabbits would choose. We had had a productive afternoon and I had come home bearing several trophies for the pot.

The next morning the plain was shrouded in a clammy mist which even in summer could sometimes precede a long hot day; but the sun had dispersed it by the time Léon appeared. He covered his balding head with a straw boater circled by a tartan ribbon, seized a cane from the collection of sticks in the hall and strode off, moving purposefully down into the plain in order to inspect what he called 'the site of discord'. The professor walked fast; the ribbon round his hat fluttered out behind him, and from time to time I had to break into a trot in order to keep pace.

It was by now very warm and little beads of sweat soon appeared on the professor's face. As we crossed the narrow bridge over the stream which wound across the plain, a snipe flew from under our feet and zigzagged away over the water. Larks, disturbed as we passed, rose and hovered above us, crying shrilly until they could safely fall back into the harvested fields. The light over the plain was dazzlingly clear, no longer diffused by the haze of high summer. But Léon seemed indifferent to nature's charms, and we pressed on without pause.

Ten minutes later the path took a bend and we came across a gate on our right. It was closed with a heavy padlock and chain, while scrawled in chalk along the top bar were the words 'Entry Forbidden'. Beyond the gate lay a grassy track which passed through a hedge into a field.

'Aha.' Léon peered over the gate. 'So here we have one ultimatum. Now let us see the other.' With surprising agility he climbed the bars of the gate and jumped down into the field. We had almost reached the hedge when there was a hoarse cry from behind us, and turning back I saw the unshaven face of Bommaert, surmounted by a greasy cap. He was gesturing wildly at the professor.

'You there, can't you read?' he cried. 'There is no right of way.'

Léon seemed nonplussed for a moment; then he walked back to the gate.

'University Professor Léon Dufour,' he said, raising his hat and extending his hand to Bommaert over the top bar. 'I am making an enquiry into the situation here on behalf of Mademoiselle Yvonne.'

'You are, are you?' The farmer looked him up and down, but made no move to take the outstretched hand. 'Well, I know nothing about that. But let me tell you that you are standing on my land without my permission. I'll trouble you to leave at once.'

I thought Léon was going to protest. Instead he said mildly, 'In that case, maybe you will open the gate.'

'My gate stays locked,' retorted Bommaert, 'and you can leave just as you came.' He turned away and marched off towards his farm.

Léon looked at me with a pained smile. 'That was not, I

think, the best moment to discuss the merits of the case. But we have now seen literally how the land lies and had the privilege of meeting one of the parties to the dispute.' Not without dignity he climbed back over the gate and we returned more slowly to the house.

The professor spent the rest of the day in the library, emerging in the evening with a sheaf of notes closely written in a tiny, angular hand. He took up a position by the fireplace in the drawing-room and addressed the aunts as if they were a public meeting.

'Dear ladies, I have I believe found a solution to this small affair which will of course require the goodwill of the parties concerned. It will be based on the well-known principle in international law of the condominium, or joint administration of a disputed territory.' He paused. Tante Thérèse looked at him admiringly, Tante Yvonne sceptically. 'In this case the two parties will be asked to agree a five-year plan for farming the land concerned, while its cultivation will rotate each year between them. In return, the blockade will be lifted.'

'Is that not a little complicated, Léon?' enquired Thérèse timidly.

'Not at all.' Léon raised his head and stroked his wispy beard. 'It will give Bommaert and André each an interest in working as good neighbours. In order to convince them I shall of course have to set my proposal in the wider context of national and international law, using the simplest examples. As Pascal says, "Hold hard to principle, but speak the language of the people".'

Tante Yvonne snorted. 'I think even you, my dear Léon, may have some difficulty with the language of those two. But by all means please try to persuade them.'

'I will ask them to call here on Sunday morning at eleven o'clock precisely. You, my young friend, shall be my messenger; you will I hope also be present as a witness to the agreement.'

I rose early the next morning in order to catch both men at home before they vanished into the fields. Once again there was a heavy mist as I made my way first to the Bommaert farm, a collection of shabby buildings around which lay a great quantity of rusting agricultural machinery. As I entered the courtyard I saw the capacious figure of Madame Bommaert carrying some milk churns from the cowshed; she invited me into her kitchen where her husband, still unshaven and wearing a dirty shirt with no collar, baggy trousers and carpet slippers, was boxing some vegetables. He scarcely bothered to look up as I announced that Tante Yvonne would like him and André to meet the professor at the house on Sunday.

'Waste of time if you ask me,' he grunted. 'That field belongs to us and I'll keep André away from it until he returns our property. Is that clear to Mademoiselle Yvonne?'

I retreated rapidly and ten minutes later was knocking on the door of André's farmhouse, where a number of fierce-looking dogs surrounded me, barking furiously and snapping at my heels. It was opened by André, a small man with a wizened face, who bore some physical resemblance, I suddenly noticed, to the professor himself. He appeared puzzled by my message.

'Don't see what good it'll do; it's Bommaert that's breaking the law. He's no right to lock me out of my field,' he said defiantly. 'But if I can help Mademoiselle Yvonne make him see sense I'll be there.'

The two farmers appeared in the drive on Sunday morning within minutes of each other. Although they had both been to Mass in the village, they chose to arrive separately. They wore almost identical shiny blue suits with stiff white collars, and their usual filthy caps had been replaced by jaunty berets which they removed as they came into the hall. Bommaert seemed an even more burly, powerful man in contrast to the short but wiry André. They eyed each other uneasily as they waited for the professor to appear. Then the door of the library swung open, and Léon beckoned them inside. He had set two straight-backed chairs before a table, and now settled himself on the other side, motioning the suspicious farmers to sit in front of him.

Léon reached for his notes, and drew a pince-nez from his waistcoat pocket. With a little cough, he began. 'I have called you here, gentlemen, at the request of your proprietor, Mademoiselle Yvonne. Some days ago she entrusted me with the task of resolving a dispute between the two of you concerning a pasture – number 42 on the property register – and the access to it. After visiting the field in question, where I may say I was most uncivilly received,' he glanced sharply at Bommaert who stared stonily back at him, 'and after much reflection, drawing on my long experience as a professor of law, I have a proposal to put to you. I believe you will both find it agreeable. But first, gentlemen, we should put your relatively minor problems in a broader framework: territorial disputes where one party seeks to exercise pressure by blockade are a familiar feature of European history. Let me give you some examples.'

The farmers stirred unhappily on their chairs as Léon droned on. It took him some ten minutes to exhaust his far-flung list of precedents and circle back to the situation nearer home, by which time Bommaert and André had begun to signal to each other in desperation. As Léon outlined his proposed solution I could see that he had lost the attention of his listeners whose only visible concern was to escape from the room as soon as they could. Neither had so far spoken a word.

'So I think you can see, gentlemen, that my proposal not only strikes a fair balance between the interests of the two of you, but is founded on international precept and example.' Léon was winding up. 'May I ask you to discuss it between yourselves and let me know what you think of the suggested way forward?'

Bommaert and André looked at each other hastily. 'Agreed,' they said, almost simultaneously, and moved to rise from their chairs. Léon remained seated.

'One moment,' he cried, leaning forward over the table. 'Should we not set out the detail of our agreement? There are some points which you would do well to write down; I stand ready of course to assist you at a further meeting.'

'Not necessary,' grunted André, looking at Bommaert. 'He and I know our minds.'

Léon looked disappointed. 'I strongly advise a document. But if you insist . . .' he turned to a bottle of red wine and some glasses on a tray behind him. 'In that case let us drink to the restoration of harmony between your two families.' He handed across the table two brimming glasses which were emptied in one draught by each farmer. Silently they rose, shook his hand perfunctorily and left the room. Léon looked thoughtfully after them.

'Our friends are not loquacious. But you see how reason can be made to overcome prejudice.' He smiled. 'Tomorrow we will verify what they are doing about their agreement.'

The professor savoured his achievement by repeating in full at the lunch table the lecture he had delivered to the unfortunate farmers. He was congratulated on all sides: even Tante Yvonne had to concede that Léon's approach appeared in this case to have been effective and she thanked him for his efforts. Tante Thérèse forgot her shyness and even proposed a toast to Léon's success.

The following afternoon the professor despatched me with the instruction discreetly to ascertain whether there were yet signs of the farmers having made peace. As I neared the gate I observed that the padlock had been removed; but before I could turn back, Bommaert emerged from a field nearby, and came down the lane towards me, his features creased in a sickly smile.

'So he sent you here already to spy on us, did he?' His manner was sarcastic. 'Well, as you can see, the gate is open; you can go back to the château and tell him that. By the way,' he came closer and gave me a crafty look, 'when is your Mr Know-All leaving you?'

I replied that Léon was departing that week. He gave a dry laugh and turned away.

The day before his departure Léon and Thérèse returned from their afternoon walk and announced to Tante Yvonne that they had become engaged. Thérèse did not say a great deal but she looked quietly happy as Léon, visibly elated, spoke of their future plans. Both they and Tante Yvonne immediately offered a home to Mathilde who responded that she would prefer to spend a few months in the Loire before deciding what to do. Her thin cheeks and slightly protruding teeth normally gave her a predatory air but on this occasion she appeared subdued and for a time the torrent of words to which we were accustomed subsided.

Only a few days later an errand on behalf of Tante Yvonne took me back down the lane past the disputed field. As I came up to the gate I saw that it was again padlocked and that fresh chalk had been applied to the notice. I stared in disbelief and then ran all the way back to the house to report what I had seen. Breathlessly I burst into the drawing-room where Yvonne was sitting alone in the window writing a letter, glasses as always on the end of her nose. She listened to my announcement with an ironic smile.

'I feared as much,' she said with a little laugh, 'but I do not think André will quickly come here to complain. I know those two: they would rather keep up their quarrel than accept a solution from outside. But they would have agreed to anything rather than return to hear another dissertation from our dear Léon. I wonder if his fondness for quotations includes my own favourite maxim of La Rochefoucauld: *"Les hommes ne vivraient pas longtemps en société, s'ils n'etaient pas dupes les uns des autres".* *

'But not a word to Thérèse, now that she has at last made up her mind to share her life with so great an intellect.'

* Men would not survive in society for long if they were not fooled by each other.

## VII  *Tante Lise*

Tante Lise's routine never varied. You knew at any moment of the day where you could find her – saying her prayers morning and evening in the chapel, feeding her animals, or tending the kitchen garden, which we called 'Lise's garden'. Winter and summer she wore the same antique felt hat, designed to ward off sun and rain alike. She was also our timekeeper, tugging on a long rope in the kitchen a quarter of an hour before lunch or dinner to toll the bell in the roof which could be heard in the farthest corner of the property and indeed up in the village. We sensed Lise watching over our day. Children who hurt themselves ran first to her for comfort; and when their elders felt in need of her silent understanding they would gravitate towards the kitchen in order to sit at the oak table while she clattered round to produce a pot of black and usually tepid tea.

One morning, when Lise sought me out for my usual talk with Tante Yvonne, she asked me to come and see her after lunch. She looked faintly conspiratorial and tried to whisper but her voice, always pitched too loud, echoed along the terrace.

I found her carefully packing a large basket with provisions: eggs, butter, bread and a ham whose bulk and weight proved to be the reason for my summons. After covering the food with a white cloth, Lise put on her black felt hat, instructed her cocker spaniel to remain on its cushion under the table, and asked me to come with her 'on a visit'. The basket was heavy and I hoped we did not have far to go but Lise gave me no hint of our destination.

We slipped through the kitchen garden, steering clear of the hives humming with activity as the bees brought in their summer harvest, and walked down a path through the tall grass of the meadow to a white gate into the road. Below lay a cluster of houses and a church, where I hoped we might stop, but Lise pressed on through the hamlet, her steps firm but her figure so bent that her eyes appeared fixed only on her feet.

The road was winding into the plain when we halted at a neat house of red brick, with a slate roof and grey shutters. For the first time Lise looked at me and smiled.

'Here at last,' she croaked, patting my arm and then knocking on the door, which was opened at once by a tiny, frail white-haired woman whose alert, intelligent face and rimless glasses gave the impression of a retired schoolmistress. She greeted Lise without surprise but with evident pleasure, and took the basket from me without comment. No introductions were made.

'Will Mademoiselle and the young man have coffee?' She showed us into a small sitting-room, facing on to the road. The room was so over-furnished that you could scarcely move but Lise, clearly at home, shuffled past the little tables covered with ornaments to a high-backed chair by the fireplace into which she at once subsided, picking up a black-covered devotional book that lay open on a table beside it and reaching in her pocket for her glasses. As I stood, awkwardly looking round, I noticed that every one of the many framed photographs in the room was of a member of the family, with several of Tante Yvonne and Lise at different times in their lives. One, a studio portrait enveloped in black crêpe, of a good-looking youth, I recognised as a picture of Antoine.

Lise gestured to a chair with a smile and then bent over her book, her lips moving slightly as she began to read. She payed no further attention as I turned back into the hall and followed the noise of cups being assembled in a kitchen which was as polished and bright as the woman herself who was now preparing the coffee. She gave me a shrewd glance.

'So you are the English lieutenant's grandson,' she said quietly. 'I remember him well; he liked it here. I am Suzanne;

I used to be the maid of Mademoiselle Lise's mother, but I was still working at the house the year he stayed. Mademoiselle must be fond of you if she has brought you here; she always comes alone.'

I asked if Lise came often.

'Oh yes, every Saturday afternoon, wet or fine. She considers the salon her own room, and has gradually brought her own things here. She thinks no one knows that she comes, but of course I have told Mademoiselle Yvonne. She always brings me these provisions; I have told her time and again that I do not need them but she insists that I do and it seems to be important to her. Joseph buys them for her in the village. She will stay now until six o'clock, reading and sleeping a little.'

I looked out across a row of lettuces at a field of maize which, like an incoming tide, swept head-high almost up to the walls of the little house. Suzanne poured me some coffee and then took a silver coffee pot to Lise. When she came back to the kitchen, she sighed.

'I was at the château when the accident happened. She was sixteen and so was I – I had only been in service a few months with her mother. She had fallen badly from her horse, and they brought her home unconscious. Then they took her away to hospital. While she was there both Madame and Monsieur her father became very ill – typhoid they thought it was – and by the time Mademoiselle Lise returned, they were both dead. For weeks Mademoiselle refused to leave her room or speak to us, and then, when she did come downstairs again she had become quite deaf. Of course Mademoiselle Yvonne took charge of her, but she has always clung to me. I only hope that when our time comes she goes before I do, even though I shall miss her grievously.'

A few minutes later I returned to the little sitting-room. Lise was sitting motionless, her book in her lap. Her head was bent forward and she appeared already to be asleep. I went quietly out of the house and made my way back up the road to the gate into the meadow. As I came along the grassy path to the lawn I saw Tante Yvonne seated under a large magnolia tree, with Lise's brown spaniel at her feet. Her chair was placed so that she could look out on the plain but she was so still that I thought she must be dozing. Nonetheless as I crept by, trying not to disturb her, she turned her head and called me over to her.

'I can guess where you have been,' she said with a smile. 'I call it the Confessional. How is Suzanne? She cares for Lise so gently; Lise never talks to me about her visits, but I can see that they bring her peace of mind.' She looked down at the spaniel. 'And her little friend always comes to find me whenever Lise goes visiting.' She paused and then spoke again in a more serious voice.

'My sister is a very saintly person, you know. Of course she is set in her ways and can be difficult, but ever since her accident more than sixty years ago she has devoted every day to us all; indeed, I sometimes see her life as one prayer to her Creator. She always wanted to live in a convent but her handicap was too great; so she decided to serve us instead. Go to her room now, if you want to understand.'

I went inside and up the broad stairs to the second floor

where Lise's room lay at the end of the corridor. Despite her absence I knocked, waited and then opened the door cautiously. The room was narrow with a low ceiling and a window looking over the plain. The walls and ceiling were white; there was a chest with a crucifix, and a prie-dieu by the narrow bed. No picture or ornament was to be seen.

I entered and sat for a moment on the bed. At that hour the house was quiet and the silence in the room was almost physical. I looked out of the window at the juxtaposition of plain and sky on which Lise had gazed for virtually every day of her eighty years. How, I wondered, in her isolated, soundless world had she coped with the violent disruption to her life which war and occupation of the house had twice caused her? Yet if her sister had protected her during her moments of greatest vulnerability she had surely returned this service a hundredfold.

That evening, when I went to my room, I found a slip of paper pinned to my pillow. On it was written in a shaky, yet upright and legible hand: 'Tante Lise asks for the greatest discretion!'

Now that I shared Lise's secret, she enjoyed giving me other tasks. One morning I arrived in the kitchen to find gloves and secateurs carefully laid out for me: then she led me to some climbing roses in her garden which needed pruning. On another, I was asked to collect butter and eggs for Suzanne from one of the nearby farms. Sometimes I would climb to a butcher at the end of the village to be handed a special parcel of meat for the dogs.

Several weeks after we had visited Suzanne, Lise opened a cupboard in the kitchen where rows of keys hung from the shelves. Taking one marked '*Notre Dame du Lac*', she handed it to me with a request to go to a little shrine which bordered a path that ran behind the lake. It contained an old wooden statue of the Virgin and Child which I was to bring back to the house where it was kept during the autumn and winter months.

'Take good care,' she said, stroking my arm, 'it is a precious relic which I always put in my room for safekeeping.'

Only a few days previously, I had discovered that the shrine served periodically as a place of pilgrimage for the family. I was lying by the lake one evening, peering into its green depths, when I heard the approaching sound of voices singing raggedly as people descended the path from the house. A small procession emerged from the trees: Father Philippe was moving slowly, reading aloud prayers from his missal and followed by the aunts walking in pairs: Lise and Florence, Alice and Thérèse, with Mathilde and several children, some of whom were carrying flowers, bringing up the rear. Each recitation was punctuated by the same chorus:

Ave, Ave, Ave Maria,
Ave, Ave, Ave Maria!

I sat up on the bank as they processed along the other side of the lake and up a grassy ride in the direction of the chapel. A child looked back and waved to me; then the singing faded into the distance. Later Father Philippe told me that each year the aunts liked to observe with this excursion the 'Novena', the nine days leading up to the mid-August festival of the Virgin.

When, at Lise's behest, I set off with the key, it was for once a thundery afternoon, with dark masses of cloud lying on the horizon to the west. As I walked past the lake I saw that the fish were rising everywhere. I pressed on to the little chapel in the field whose single window under a simple round arch was covered by a grille through which the passer-by had to peer if he wished to see the altar with its vase of dried flowers, and the figure of the Virgin. I unlocked a small door at the back and, slipping in, carefully lifted the statue. The Virgin wore a long blue robe, its folds skilfully carved, and had a gold crown on her head. She was looking down at the infant Christ, whom she carried in the crook of one arm.

Bearing the statue in front of me as if it were porcelain, I made my way back past the lake. A huge carp rose only a few feet away. Today seemed a wonderful opportunity to make a good catch after several lean weeks when I had returned to the house empty-handed.

I set the statue carefully down under the tree in which I kept hidden my two primitive fishing rods and bait, and having armed my favourite rod, walked cautiously down to the lake, trembling with anticipation. Nor was I disappointed: within seconds I had caught a good-sized fish and, progressing slowly along the bank, I took two others only minutes later. Holding them by their tails I carried the carp back to the tree. Then, as I laid them out on the grass, I saw that the statue had gone.

For a moment I stood still, nonplussed. Then in a growing panic I ran up and down, searching for the statue under the neighbouring bushes and trees. But I knew that I had not mistaken where I had left it in the grass. I sat under the tree and buried my head in my arms. Could an animal have taken it? But I had heard nothing. Was it perhaps possessed of some supernatural power, and had it flown back to the shrine? Clutching at any hope I ran back down the path to the chapel and, shading my eyes, looked hopefully through the grille. But apart from the flowers and a gilt cross, the altar stood empty. I returned to the tree, praying as I ran that during my absence the statue might have returned as inexplicably as it had vanished. My prayer was not answered: the three dead fish lay where I had left them, their glassy eyes staring vacantly up at me.

With a sense of despair I realised that I must return to the house and admit my negligence. Her deafness would prevent Lise from understanding my story; I would have to write it down for her. This, however, would only serve to emphasise how I had betrayed her trust. Valuable as the statue might be, it was the thought that I would forfeit her confidence which gave me the greatest anguish.

Twice more, as I reached the end of the lake, I returned to the spot where I had left the statue and then, finally accepting that the age of miracles was over, at least as far as this terrible day was concerned, I crept up the drive. The clouds were now overhead, and the first heavy drops of rain were falling, raising a haze of dust on the road and the gravel. There was a roll of thunder in the distance. At my wits' end, I made my way through a side door into the kitchen. I fervently hoped that Lise would not be there; at least this would give me time to compose my story.

As I came into the darkened kitchen I at once saw the statue standing on a shelf by the window. Below it sat Christian studiously drinking coffee from a bowl; Lise was rummaging over the stove.

My relief was so intense that my knees gave way and I sat down abruptly at the table. Christian ignored my presence, drinking noisily with a spoon, his eyes fixed ruminatively on the statue. Lise placed a pot of tea on the table and brought me a cup; she seemed incurious to know what might have happened, the safe arrival of her treasure being the only important event that afternoon. Nor did I feel like trying to tell her, at the top of my voice, of my bewilderment at what had happened.

Towards Christian I felt a wave of anger, but it seemed equally useless to vent my rage or to seek an explanation. Had he, like some magpie, simply lighted on the statue and spirited it away to the house without further thought? Or had he wanted to play a joke on me of which his total unconcern at my presence was now a part? I went over and stood opposite him, trying to stare into his face.

'Christian,' I said quietly, 'you have just made me very frightened. Please never do that again.' He looked up, his transparent blue eyes expressionless. Then he smiled and gestured to the statue. 'It is beautiful,' he said.

That night, I found myself for a moment alone in the kitchen with Lise. She drew a hot brick from the range in order to warm Tante Yvonne's bed. Then she draped a grey cloth over the cage of her canaries. These rites completed, she turned to me and took my hand.

'Thank you for bringing back our Virgin and Child today,' she managed for once to whisper. 'She watches over this house. But, you know, we have to watch over her as well.'

## VIII  *Bob*

The telephone was not an instrument which was frequently used in the house. Making even a local call was a hazardous affair, and involved connections through the village switchboard on a line which was faint and subject to interruptions in the slightest atmospheric disturbance. Outward calls were in any case discouraged as extravagant and unnecessary, only to be made in emergencies, while the harsh, almost violent ringing of the bell never failed to produce a general movement of alarm.

It was late one night when Madeleine answered the telephone, and after a few moments came to fetch me. 'It's Bob,' she said gravely, 'he has something to ask you.'

We had not seen much of Bob, Florence's elder son, during his brother's short but turbulent visit. Maybe he sensed trouble and preferred not to become drawn into François' difficulties. Normally, however, he was a regular member of the household, if usually away during the week working for a firm of shipping brokers at a port near Dunkirk, a job which, I gathered, had been found for him by his mother after the war.

Short and stocky where François was tall and gangling, Bob and his brother bore little resemblance to each other. Bob's most obvious characteristic was a shock of prematurely grey hair, virtually white in places, which sat oddly on a man in his early thirties and was a source of some embarrassment to him. He affected a number of English – or, as he preferred to say, Anglo-Saxon – habits such as the heavy tweeds with their 'Prince of Wales' check which he liked to wear at work or on Sundays, the Craven 'A' cigarettes he smoked when not puffing one of his large collection of pipes, and his religious observance of *le five o'clock,* a pause for tea which brought to a halt anything else he was doing, however important. His Anglomania extended to his dog, Hector, a snappish terrier of indeterminate breed whom he addressed in a heavily accented English – 'seet' or 'com 'eer' – and which he took everywhere, often carrying him under his arm. Hector's temper was not improved by the long hours he endured in Bob's car when Bob was at work, his landlady having categorically refused to consider any more accommodating arrangement.

Bob was a frustrated sailor. He had spent the early part of

the war as a midshipman in the navy and had been with the French fleet at Mers-el-Kébir when it had been sunk by Admiral Somerville, an episode which he recounted to me at length and on several occasions. Sucking at his pipe, he drew me a sketch one evening of the disposition of the French ships in the port and of the manoeuvres of the *Hood* and the other British vessels as they opened fire. It was, he maintained, the ultimate act of perfidy by *la perfide Albion*, intent on achieving once and for all naval supremacy over her ancient French rival.

After the war fate was unkind to Bob. He failed several medical tests and had to abandon all thought of a naval career. The girl he had met in Algiers had married another officer, and, discouraged by this early romantic setback, he seemed disinclined to look elsewhere for a wife, much to his mother's disappointment. His comfortable routine at work and the companionship of Hector were, it seemed, enough to satisfy his wants. Moreover Bob was at his happiest driving over the plain in his little Renault looking for churches or cottages with some distinctive feature which he would photograph. He was indeed a most assiduous photographer, although the family were rarely favoured with the chance to view the product of his labours which took the form of accumulating boxes of slides stowed carefully away in his room.

He would on occasion invite me to accompany him on these expeditions which he always meticulously planned by studying in detail the yellow-covered Michelin road maps and charting our route as if we were embarking on a long sea voyage rather than an afternoon's excursion. Nor, once we were in motion, was it permissible for us to deviate from the chosen route, however tempting the prospect we might chance upon during our trip. Kilometres covered and petrol used were always precisely noted when we returned to the house, in an exercise book kept in the car.

Despite his absorption with his photographic activities, Bob felt a strong responsibility for the maintenance of the estate. Indeed, he nursed the illusion that the place would fall to pieces without him, although he was not himself a keen gardener and, unlike even Oncle Auguste, could not often be found actually wielding gardening implements. His instructions to Joseph and Christian, issued during his frequent rather grand strolls round the property, with Hector at his heels, were erratic and were usually either ignored or surreptitiously corrected behind his back by Madeleine once he had returned to work.

The corridor was dark and draughty as I made my way to the telephone.

'Bob?'

There was a long silence, punctuated by crackles and a loud humming on the line.

'Bob, are you there?' I repeated.

'Hector's dead.' Bob's voice sounded faint and subdued. 'Run over by a car this morning. It's a great shock; he was such a friend.'

I found some words of consolation.

'You were fond of Hector, weren't you?' asked Bob anxiously. 'I admire the English for their love of animals. Of course we must give him a proper burial; I suggest tomorrow night. You will find his blanket in my room, and ask Joseph for a spade. I will drive directly to the big tulip tree by the lake and meet you there at ten. But only you.'

I went back into the salon and told Florence, who was putting away her sewing, what Bob intended to do.

She looked thoughtful, while Madeleine laughed, not unsympathetically.

'Poor Bob,' she said, 'how will he survive without Hector? We shall have to find another companion for him.'

The next day was sweltering. In the early evening I went up to Bob's room on the top floor in search of Hector's blanket. The room was dark and hot, and I threw open the shutters and windows to let in some air. Bob's pipes were wedged in a rack beside various naval artefacts, as well as pictures of the vessels in which he had sailed. His collection of old cameras was arranged neatly on a shelf, above which there hung a striking photograph in a dark frame of the lake under snow, of which he had once given me a copy. Hector's basket, in which lay a neatly folded brown blanket, was in one corner, tucked behind a handsome *lit bateau* that took up much of the space. It was a shabby, comfortable place where I always felt at home when invited in by Bob while he treated himself to a dram – invariably a glass of neat whisky from the copious supply he kept in a cupboard. He liked a good yarn, and if his stories of the war and North Africa seemed occasionally rather far-fetched, he nonetheless always held my attention.

As ten o'clock approached and the aunts were preparing to

retire, I slipped out of the front door with the blanket on one arm and Joseph's spade on my shoulder. I made my way along the drive to the point where a track turned off, falling sharply down to the lake. It was a still, warm night with a clear sky, but under the trees it was very dark and I regretted not having thought to bring any light. As I stumbled down the path bushes and thickets, magnified by the gloom, reared up at me. But I knew my way well and reached the bank without mishap, walking along it to the big tree at the far end where water trickled through a sluice to form a stream below.

I stood under the tulip tree and waited. There was not a breath of air to ripple the water, and the moon which had now risen from behind the hill was clearly reflected on its still surface. A nightjar churred; and at one moment some creature disturbed the ducks sleeping on the bank, for they suddenly set up a quacking before just as abruptly falling silent again. Above me, in the darkness, the clock in the church tower struck the hour. I looked round anxiously, hoping that Bob would not be too late.

His car was distinctly audible from a distance as it laboured up the first long slope from the plain. I imagined the little Renault swaying as it took each bend in the road and heard the motor idle while Bob opened the white wooden gates to the ride which led along the edge of the wood. Then the headlights appeared, picking out the rough grass and scattering some grazing rabbits as the car descended the slope to the lake.

Despite the warm evening Bob was wearing a peaked cap and blue jacket which made him look like a seaman on shore leave. He shook hands a little formally and reached into his pocket for his pipe which he thrust into his mouth unlit before casting round for a suitable spot for Hector's grave. Eventually he settled on a slope under a large rock overlooking the lake and began to dig. Next he fetched the diminutive brown and white corpse of Hector from the back of the car and, wrapping it in the blanket, laid it reverently at the bottom of the hole. Taking turns we shovelled back the earth. The interment completed, we sat down on a bank by the water and Bob lit his pipe.

'Nice of you to help,' he said, turning his liquid brown eyes and mournful, somewhat canine features towards me, his grey hair glistening in the moonlight. 'No one understands what great company Hector was. Poor old chap, he deserved a decent burial. Did I tell you about the time we buried the captain's hound at sea with full naval honours?' Bob clearly needed to talk. We moved along the bank and eventually reached the green rowing-boat which was moored to a small wooden landing-stage. He put in the rowlocks, inserted the oars and, motioning me to sit in the stern, cast off. Perched on the thwart facing me, he began gently to row, water falling in translucent drops from his oars. We created scarcely any wake as the boat glided over the glassy surface.

'Mother wants me to move to Toulon and find a better job there,' said Bob after a long silence, as we drifted across the water, 'but I can't leave here – too much to do to keep the property in order. Joseph's too old, and it's no use relying on Christian. Besides . . .' he did not complete the sentence, but it was not difficult to imagine what he was thinking. Why should he abandon his comfortable routine and the place where he was supremely content, to face the uncertainties of a strange city, and in the name of an ambition he did not feel? I pictured the years passing, with Bob growing increasingly like Oncle Auguste, pottering aimlessly from month to month in his secluded kingdom. No doubt this image had crossed Florence's mind, too.

'Of course it would be nice to marry and have a son.' Bob was clearly pursuing his train of thought. 'Someone to take over this place one day. But that's too late for me now.' He spoke as if he was in his sixties rather than still well under forty. 'At my time of life you can't harness yourself to a fresh cart,' he concluded obscurely.

We rowed back to the shore and Bob made fast.

'Thanks for your help,' he repeated. 'Couldn't have done it alone,' he added through the window as he turned the car round.

I made my way back along the lakeside and up the path to the house. The shutters were closed and there was no light to help me as I felt my way up the steps to the front door. It was locked. I went round to the side and tried at the kitchen, with no success. Wondering if I was condemned to spend the night outside, I moved along the terrace, looking up at the windows. Like some great ship moored at a quayside, the house confronted me with its silent, massive presence. To my relief, I saw a chink of light behind the shutters of Madeleine's room and threw a small stone to attract her attention. One shutter was pushed back and her blonde head appeared. Moments later she was in the hall, apologising for Lise's forgetfulness.

'You do Bob a favour and find yourself locked out for your pains.' She stood smiling, facing me at the foot of the stairs, her hair falling dishevelled on her shoulders, and I noticed that I was almost as tall as she. At that moment my heart seemed to turn over. She gave me her hand to say goodnight but I held on to it and for a second tried to pull her towards me. Startled, she drew back, and then, smiling again, she bent forward and kissed my cheek.

'What an exciting evening you have had,' she said lightly as I stood, embarrassed and confused. 'Time you had some sleep.'

We climbed the long staircase side by side. Her grey dressing-gown, rather too long, trailed behind her. As we reached her door on the first floor she turned and put her hands on my shoulders.

'You are growing up,' she murmured. She gave me another soft kiss and, before I could react, she slipped inside. I raced on up the stairs treading on air.

For a long time I lay awake, floating on a wave which felt exhilarating, warm, comforting. Why could not my life here go on for ever, unchanging and secure? I pictured myself spending long evenings seated happily between Tante Yvonne and Florence; and unending days outside with Bob or driving back and forth across the plain with Madeleine. Eventually I would have my own allotted place here, and would belong to this world as much as they did. But when at length I fell asleep I dreamed that I was hunting for Madeleine through one empty room after another, desperate to find her before some unseen pursuer, bent on snatching me away, caught up with me.

The next morning I went in search of Madeleine. I found her deep in conversation with Florence in the big upstairs drawing-room, but as I turned to go Florence told me to sit down.

'We were discussing Bob's future,' she said with a smile. 'Madeleine agrees with me that he needs a change. I know my cousin could find him a better post than his present one, if only he was prepared to move to Toulon. In any case, a move would do him good.'

I sat silent while mother and daughter continued to discuss the tactics of persuading Bob to go. As I listened to them I felt depressed, almost panic-stricken.

'No, you shouldn't do it,' I burst out suddenly. They both looked at me in surprise, having, I think, half forgotten my presence.

'I am sorry, Tante Florence, I did not want to interrupt. But Bob . . . he's happy here,' I murmured lamely. I did not have the eloquence to explain myself, nor did I want to talk about what he had said to me the previous night. That was between the two of us.

An irritated expression crossed Madeleine's face.

'Well, you are his friend, maybe you know best what is right for him,' she said with a touch of sarcasm.

'I didn't mean that,' I replied unhappily.

'Then don't upset yourself,' she smiled. 'In the end, Bob will decide for himself what he wants to do.'

'I always liked taking decisions,' remarked Florence, pick-

ing up her sewing, 'but some people seem to find it so difficult. Bob takes too much after your father,' she added, looking
at Madeleine. '"Never decide today what you can put off until
tomorrow" was poor Henri's precept.'

She glanced across the room at me. 'Perhaps you are right.
We shall see. And if I cannot succeed in securing my son
another job, we had better at least find him a new dog!'

In the weeks that followed, Bob seemed to go into something of a decline. As before, he spent his weekends and days
off with us, but he had lost much of his appetite for walking
or driving and would sit for long hours in the salon with Tante
Yvonne, distractedly turning the pages of old editions of
*L'Illustration.* There was no mention of a change of job and I
deduced that Florence's approaches, if she had made them,
had been rebuffed.

One night, after everyone had retired and I was endeav-
ouring to read in my room by the light of a small table
lamp, I heard a creaking in the passage outside my door. At
first I paid no attention, since the wood in the old house
was constantly shifting and giving off sharp cracking noises
which initially had always startled me. Now, however, I
detected steps on the staircase and, quietly opening the door,
I was just in time to see the outline of Bob's head and shoulders descending to the floor below. I slipped out and peered
over the banisters. By the single light in the passage I could
see Bob stepping rigidly along the landing until he turned
down the next flight of stairs. Something about his bearing
seemed unnatural, and he looked neither to right nor left.

Then I realised that he must be sleepwalking.

Years of communal living at school had accustomed me to
boys talking and on occasion even walking in their sleep, but
schoolboy lore dictated that it was damaging, even dangerous,
to rouse a sleepwalker. There seemed no choice therefore but
to follow Bob and at least ensure that he came to no harm.
I threw on a dressing-gown and crept downstairs. Before I
could reach the ground floor, however, there was a tremen-
dous crash from the direction of the kitchen. I raced down the
remaining steps and along the corridor to the kitchen door,
switching on lights as I went. Bob was sitting on the floor in
a daze, having collided with a chair in the dark. As I helped
him to his feet I heard the disembodied voice of Tante Alice
enquiring querulously from above who was there.

'It's all right, Tante Alice, I'm in the kitchen with Bob.'

'Well, you're waking the whole house.' She retreated crossly
to her room. I was reminded of the episode with Oncle
Auguste in the village square: she had never thanked me for
the assistance I had given him on that remarkable morning
and I felt disinclined to ask for her help now, despite Bob's
obviously confused state.

I levered Bob on to a chair and asked him if he would like
a glass of water. His request for whisky instead indicated a
rapid return to his more normal condition. I slipped into the
dining-room and poured out a generous measure from Tante
Alice's camouflaged bottle. When I returned we gravitated to
the kitchen table. Copper pans in all shapes and sizes hung
round the walls and shone dully in the dim light of a single

overhead lamp; while the quiet in the house magnified the ticking of a tall corner clock, whose heavy weights were wound up every night by Lise.

'I've not been quite myself recently,' said Bob, leaning forward on his elbows. 'Things have been rather on top of me. It's a difficult decision, but I think I'm going back to sea. Merchant shipping, of course, and a fairly junior grade to start with, but I need the change.'

This was so different from Bob's earlier attitude that I showed my surprise.

'I couldn't have faced another office job, but the sea is different. I had an offer from an old mess-mate yesterday; we served together in North Africa and now he's a captain in the merchant navy. It's strange – he rang right out of the blue. I said I'd sleep on it, and I suppose that's what I'm doing now.' He laughed a little sheepishly.

'Naturally I'll have to ask my mother and Tante Yvonne what they think. I'm worried about leaving the house, of course, but everyone seems to want me to go.'

He drained his whisky and we moved back upstairs. As usual, Bob shook hands with me a little solemnly before retreating to his room.

'Not often one says goodnight twice in the same evening,' he remarked. 'It was good of you to turn out for me; I always seem to rely on you in a tight corner.'

The next morning, as I perched on the terrace steps, Madeleine came and sat beside me.

'Well, that's Bob's immediate future sorted out,' she said

with a grin. 'We shall all miss him of course, not least you I suppose, but it was a last chance to get him out of his rut.'

'You mean his friend's call was not . . . ?'

'No. Mother can be very determined when she wants: she has been working on this for some time, but you must promise not to tell Bob or he may change his mind again. We can trust you with our secret, can't we?'

She gave me a long look, and pressed my hand.

There was a pause. Then her expression changed: it became sullen, almost mutinous as she looked down at her feet. She hunched her shoulders and pushed out her chin although the effect was softened by the hair which strayed over her forehead in a fringe.

'I only wish mother could think in the same way about me,' she muttered. 'I need to go away too, but that is something she refuses to understand.'

Several days later I was in Bob's room while he packed a kitbag before leaving for Brest from where, after a period of training, he would board ship.

'Look,' he said, as he took down his pipes, 'I shall expect you to keep a weather eye on things here for me. You'll be back before I am, I suppose, and next time I'd like you to move into my room. It's comfortable enough in here, so make yourself at home. We have been pretty good shipmates, you and I.'

## IX  Agathe

'It is time', said Tante Yvonne to me one evening, 'that you visited the panther. Do you not agree, Thérèse?'

'Most certainly. It is important to cultivate the mind,' responded Thérèse with a twinkle in her eye. 'I will send her a message suggesting that she issues an invitation to tea. That is the hour she likes to receive callers.'

The panther was, Yvonne explained to me, Agathe Chaillot who lived alone in the largest house on the main street of the village. Some years ago she had for no particular reason taken to her bed and liked to spend her days reading, or supposedly writing memoirs which in Yvonne's view were unlikely ever to find their way on to the printed page.

'She will tell you about her life and incidentally no doubt a great deal about ours,' said Yvonne. 'Don't believe everything you hear; and don't let her give you more books than you can carry away,' she added.

On the chosen day I pulled the bell handle of an imposing house whose windows fronted directly on to the narrow main street. The door was opened by a tiny maid of indeterminate age who eyed me suspiciously before allowing me inside. But she appeared to be expecting me, acknowledging my presence without speaking a word before she left me standing in a hall panelled in heavily varnished wood and almost devoid of light. The air had the heavy, fusty smell with a distinct element of mothballs that I had come recently to associate with the hermetically sealed doors and windows inside which French people apparently preferred to live. Silently, the maid reappeared at the top of the stairs, and with a curt nod invited me to follow her.

I was shown into a large, sunny room with a huge bed standing along the windows at the far end. The woman who was leaning against an array of pillows, from which emanated a strong scent of lavender, seemed to me unnaturally thin and frail even for her considerable age: I noticed her smooth, almost transparent skin, her sunken cheeks and her sharp, humorous eyes. She had neat white hair and looked poised and elegant, but there was a feline air about her movements which no doubt accounted for her sobriquet.

'Now find a chair and tell me how everyone is below,' said

Madame Chaillot when I had shaken the skeletal hand she extended to me. 'Of course I keep an eye on you all, as you can observe.' She noticed with amusement my surprise as, approaching the window, I found that I could see beyond the massive village wall at the end of the garden and down to the roof of the house which looked as if it was anchored to the edge of the plain. It was a spectacular view, almost vertiginous, as if you were looking out over a vast expanse of ocean from the mast of a ship.

'I'm afraid I have not seen Yvonne for more than a year,' said Madame Chaillot as I moved a chair up to the bed. 'As you can see, I am not as mobile as I once was. But by reading I can still travel great distances. And I enjoy living with the past: it is a virtue not a vice to do so. Make sure, I beg you, that you retain memories of your youth.'

She paused, narrowing her eyes in thought. 'Ah, one's youth! The world was so different before the Great War. I remember it now as one long, final party before the curtain fell. That was how things seemed down at the house, too – tennis, boating on the lake, dancing to the gramophone. Antoine and Henri led the way, always encouraged by Yvonne of course; they loved to keep the place full. Friends came from Paris and stayed for weeks. I met my late husband there and married in the same summer as Thérèse.' She drew back her lips in a curious, somewhat disconcerting grimace.

'After the war it was so different. Antoine was dead and poor Henri badly injured. Then my husband died, too: he was a changed man when he came back from the trenches and I think he never recovered from the shock of losing so many of his friends.'

The door opened and the maid appeared carrying a tea-tray which she placed on a table by Madame Chaillot. There was tea in perforated silver balls on which you poured the hot water, and a rectangular fruit cake of a kind I had seen in the *patissier* in the square. As the maid silently withdrew, Madame Chaillot remarked, 'Monique is hardly talkative, and she has an uncertain temper. But she has been with me since I married, so by now we have learnt to rub along together well enough.'

I looked round the room. Bookshelves lined one of the walls, and were crammed with volumes in all shapes and sizes. In a corner stood a desk liberally strewn with papers, while a fire flickered in the large hearth, despite the warmth of the afternoon. Following my glance, the panther drew back her lips again in what I realised was the nearest she could come to a smile.

'Now tell me what you are reading. What amuses someone of your age these days?'

I replied that I was making progress with *The Three Musketeers,* a volume which Tante Alice had picked out of the library for me and which I was, in truth, finding rather heavy-going. Madame Chaillot snorted.

'Rubbish. We must begin to awaken your sensibilities with some real literature. You are old enough now for the greatest romantic tale of this century.' She guided me along the shelves until I found a well-thumbed, slim volume in a torn cover, which proved to be *Le Grand Meaulnes* by Alain-Fournier.

'You will, I hope, never forget that I introduced you to this wonderful story. But I will say no more; bring it back when you have read it and tell me what you think.'

Half an hour later I was dropping down the path to the house. The afternoon was fading, but not the light, and rather than head for the drive I went round to the lower gates through which I could walk back up the meadow. There was a bench at the far end under one of the great copper beeches which stood in a semi-circle guarding the approach to the house, and I settled down here to read the first pages of *Le Grand Meaulnes*. I was at once enthralled. The evening had advanced unnoticed when the clanging of the bell in the roof, announcing the approach of dinner, roused me from the new, enchanted world to which the panther had opened the door for me. Later, I read far into the night, entranced by the magical place into which Meaulnes wandered, and by his passion for its princess, Yvonne de Galais.

Only a few days later I again rang the panther's doorbell and was let into the hall by the silent Monique. This time she led me on to a large terrace overlooking the garden where, under a striped awning, Madame Chaillot was reclining on a chaise-longue. She was *en deshabillé,* wearing what to my eyes appeared to be something between a pinkish dress and a night-gown with a mass of lace at the collar. Beside her lay piles of books, and some roses floated in a bowl.

'Well?' She looked up at me expectantly. 'How did you find "the mysterious domain"? But I can see from your expression that you are still there.

'For me the house below once held a similar magic.' She sighed, looking into the green depths of the garden. 'Memory plays strange tricks as you get old; you can no longer clearly recall the order of events. The Great War, the years between and the Occupation – we have played out our lives against a sombre tapestry. I am at present engaged in putting my recollections on paper; it is an arduous but enlivening experience. Do not forget that if history takes place forwards, we are always seeing it backwards. I was writing only this morning about the invasion of 1940: has Yvonne told you about that?'

I shook my head.

'Well then, let me do so.' The panther raised herself and adjusted her cushions so as to sit upright before embarking on her story.

'Imagine a glorious, hot early summer such as we rarely have in Flanders. The fighting reached us in radiant sunshine but with a terrible suddenness: one moment we were leading our normal daily lives, the next English soldiers were streaming over the plain to the village, dirty and exhausted, with the Germans only half a day behind them. We were told that they intended to make a stand here; as you have observed, it is a natural vantage point and they wanted to protect the approaches to Dunkirk. I was alone with Monique and an officer insisted on our leaving, so we went down to Yvonne who had refused to move: she was emphatic that she was not going to abandon her house to the Germans.

'We were quite a crowd: Yvonne and her two sisters, Florence with François and Madeleine, Serge and his parents, and several of the farmers. The next morning, from the terrace, we saw a line of German tanks, guns and trucks coming over the horizon. Before long they were beginning to fire over our heads at the village, and suddenly we were in the middle of a battlefield. We took to the cellars and just afterwards there was a great crash as a shell went through the roof. Luckily it did not explode but we felt sure the house was being destroyed.

'It remained very noisy until the next afternoon. Then the guns stopped. As we were thinking of coming out, we heard footsteps above us and loud voices speaking German. Yvonne never hesitated. She picked up the cross she had taken from the chapel, and around which we had been praying that morning, and holding it in front of her she went up the steps to the kitchen.'

The panther drew back her lips. 'As a gesture it seemed a little theatrical, but it was a brave thing to do. I shall never forget the sight of a pair of very polished jackboots when I came up through the trapdoor: they belonged to a German officer who pointed his revolver at each of us as we emerged.'

Madame Chaillot paused as she conjured up the scene. 'I felt angry, frightened and humiliated all at once,' she said fiercely, 'and that cocktail became very familiar to everyone during the next four years. But on that day I think it was above all anger that dominated Yvonne. I could see her asking herself how these men dared to walk uninvited around her house. I am afraid her long calvary was only just beginning. But I am tiring you?'

Again I shook my head, this time vigorously. I had lived every second of the panther's narrative.

'Well, the Germans took over the property, but first they left one half of the house to Yvonne and the family. In '43, however, the SS arrived and everyone was given just a day to leave: so Yvonne rented a little place in the village square, which she liked to call her *boutique*: I tried to persuade her to move in here, but she was determined to keep her independence. She lived there with Lise, while Florence took the children away to Boulogne. Alarming stories would reach us about what the Germans were doing to the property. At one time they began to cut down many of the trees. Yvonne would come here and sit on this terrace looking down at her house with tears in her eyes. On each occasion she vowed that she would restore everything to what it had been before the war, but she knew that she was getting old and that it would be a harder struggle than the previous time.

'As for Lise, she took her expulsion from the house almost more badly than Yvonne. Her infirmity had made her more dependent than the rest of them on the house and its routine and I don't believe she has yet been able to forgive the Germans who inflicted such a brutal departure on her. Why, Yvonne once told me that even the sight of a dachshund . . .'

She broke off as a young man appeared on the terrace and came unhurriedly towards us. 'Jean-Jacques,' she exclaimed, looking more animated than I had hitherto seen her, 'what a pleasure. My dear nephew, you have arrived earlier than I had expected.'

'The roads were empty, Aunt Agathe.' Jean-Jacques gave me a sideways look as he bent over Madame Chaillot. He was short but thin, with narrow features and a pointed chin, and his hair was carefully parted in the middle. His otherwise immaculate white suit had been somewhat crumpled by the journey.

Introductions were made and I learned that Jean-Jacques, Madame Chaillot's only nephew, worked as an estate agent in Amiens. He seemed pleased enough to see his aunt but had to make an effort, I thought, to be agreeable to me. There was something sharp, almost sly, about his manner and I quickly took my leave clutching several books which Madame Chaillot had put on one side for me.

On my next call I was greeted by Monique with an expression that seemed even grimmer than usual.

'Madame is not well, but she wants to see you,' she vouchsafed. This being the longest sentence I had so far heard her deliver, I felt vaguely disquieted. My unease was confirmed by the sight of Madame Chaillot lying prostrate on her bed and swathed in shawls. She seemed scarcely to have the energy to proffer her hand and her eyes, when she turned her head, were moist, almost glazed.

'Oh, the battle I have had with that nephew of mine,' she said in a low voice. 'Jean-Jacques has told me he wants me to leave this house and move to Amiens. He claims it is too large for me and too expensive to run. No doubt he is right and alas he is a co-proprietor. But I know I could not survive such a move. My whole life has been here and I cannot be separated now from these walls. What is to be done?' she cried rhetorically, opening and shutting her hands on the bed like a cat pawing a blanket.

Alarmed by the panther's disarray, I did my best to distract her by plying her with more questions about the war and Occupation. But she seemed scarcely to hear me and I left, feeling angry that my new friend should be turned out of her house by someone whom I had disliked at first sight.

As I entered the drive I spied the back of Tante Thérèse deep in some bushes while she weeded one of the large oval flower-beds in which she took a particular pride. She was in her gardening clothes, with a gaily coloured straw hat to keep off the sun and a blue apron tied round her waist. I lay down on the grass next to her and told her what was happening to Madame Chaillot. She sat back on her heels as she listened to me, looking increasingly worried.

'Our poor panther. Did she tell you that we were both married in the same year? That nephew of hers is behaving appallingly, and not for the first time. His wife stirs him up as well. Of course we must try and help.'

That evening Thérèse, Yvonne and Florence sat together and talked about what they could do. I noticed that Tante Alice was not brought into the discussion. Remembering how she had only recently come close to evicting one of her own tenants, there might, I supposed, be some doubt as to where her sympathies would lie.

Tante Yvonne told me that Jean-Jacques had on several occasions sailed close to the wind in his business and was lucky not to have spent time in prison.

'He was just the same as a small boy, always taking his friends' things,' she added. 'I have no doubt he wants to make money out of Agathe Chaillot's house – maybe he has already had an offer. I fear he responds only to bribes or threats these days, so we may have to resort to both in a small way if we are to persuade him to behave decently.'

The three ladies went to work with impressive speed. An invitation was sent to Jean-Jacques to call when he was next visiting his aunt, on the pretext that Tante Yvonne wished to discuss with him the possible sale of a farmhouse. Lured by this bait, he arrived one afternoon only a few days later behind the wheel of a powerful-looking red sports car. I observed that he was wearing the same white suit as when I had last seen him.

Tante Yvonne chose to receive Jean-Jacques in the small salon, flanked by her sister and sister-in-law. In view of the panther's confidences to me she suggested that I might be a silent witness to the discussion.

Once Jean-Jacques was settled in a comfortable armchair, a cup of coffee on his knee, Thérèse opened fire with an innocent question about Madame Chaillot's health.

'She seems a little depressed at present, but she has no real problems,' responded Jean-Jacques breezily, lying back in his chair.

'Depressed?' Thérèse appeared concerned. 'I am sorry to hear that. I must come up and see her.'

'Please don't bother to do so. It really isn't necessary at present. Indeed I sometimes feel that too much company upsets Aunt Agathe.' He glanced stonily in my direction.

'I have often wondered if Agathe was not rather lonely,' intervened Florence sweetly, 'but she has always assured me that she can never feel alone in her own house, which is so full of memories for her. I envy her such roots: we are all the better for them, are we not?'

Jean-Jacques stirred uneasily in his chair.

'Maybe: but half the house is empty, and it is very large for her and me to maintain.'

Tante Yvonne looked across at him sharply. 'Does that really count against the security of living where you belong? You have never known the misfortune of being forced out of your own home, but it happened to me not long ago and I can assure you I will never forget the shock I felt. If we cannot forgive those who occupied our country for inflicting such suffering on us it should be unthinkable for us to inflict it on ourselves.' She stared intensely at him as she leaned forward, one arm on the table, the other clutching her cane.

'Really, Tante Yvonne, I do not understand this discussion. Perhaps we could now talk about the farmhouse you wish to consider selling.' Jean-Jacques began to look distinctly alarmed, turning his head with a hunted expression, as if searching for a way out of the room; but he could not see past three pairs of eyes staring unblinkingly at him.

'I think you know very well what I mean, Jean-Jacques; and I have no intention of discussing any business with you, until you have given me your word that you will not try to remove Agathe from a house she has lived in longer than you have been on this earth.'

'Arrangements between my aunt and myself concern only ourselves,' declared Jean-Jacques defiantly.

'Not when they involve taking her against her will from our village.' Tante Yvonne's eyes seemed to be starting from her head with anger and she banged her cane on the floor. 'I tell you, Jean-Jacques, that if you force out Agathe you will never be able to show your face or do any business near here again. You should reflect on that.'

'It is not fair to threaten me in this way,' replied Jean-Jacques sullenly, evidently cowed by the old lady's vehemence. 'In any case, I had made no firm plans. I do not know where these exaggerated stories come from.' Again he shot a hostile glance at me.

'Well that's settled, then: you can assure us that you have no intention of obliging Agathe to move out? If so, perhaps we can get down to business.' She looked expectantly at him.

Jean-Jacques studied the carpet at his feet. 'None at present,' he said at last reluctantly, 'although I cannot see why . . .'

'Agathe is one of my oldest friends, and what happens to her will always concern me. If that is clear to you, I do not think we need discuss the matter further,' said Tante Yvonne dismissively. 'Now, I will call Madeleine and ask her to go through with you in the library the details of our proposed sale.'

When Jean-Jacques had left, Tante Yvonne chuckled. 'We were perhaps a little severe with him, but people like Jean-Jacques need a message spelt out if they are to heed it. I think we have stopped him for the moment, but we shall have to keep our eyes open in future.'

She turned to me. 'Perhaps you will let Thérèse accompany you on your next visit to the panther; except for yourself none of us has seen as much of her recently as we should.'

The following day, however, before Thérèse and I had the opportunity to walk up the hill to Madame Chaillot, the maid Monique appeared in the drive almost buried under a huge bunch of red roses. On the accompanying card, the panther had scrawled a single word – '*Merci*'.

## X Bernadette

There were many quiet places where I could drowsily spend a summer afternoon, hidden from the house but in reality quite close to it. I preferred the overgrown shrubbery on the southern side because through the green curtains of tall grass and straggling bushes I could glimpse the plain, bathed in sunshine while I lay sheltered from the heat. With some exertion I had cleared a path through a natural barrier of undergrowth in order to create a private way into the fields and to a copse below them where the rabbits ran wild and the pigeons cooed for hours on end, invisible in the leafy branches of the trees.

On one occasion I was lying on my back in a hollowed out

nest of grass, my hands behind my head, when I heard a rustling in the bushes. Mardi, who was stretched out on her side, her back pressed against the soles of my feet, raised her head and growled softly; while a squirrel, which had been chewing at a nut on a branch above us, dropped it and flew with jerky movements higher up the tree. Turning my head I saw a woman standing motionless on the track, her eyes fixed on me. She wore a grey dress reaching down to a pair of elastic-sided boots and her unkempt hair was crowned by a black straw hat, secured by a large pin. It was a startling apparition, but somehow not a threatening one. As I scrambled to my feet, she spoke and to my surprise greeted me in English: 'Hello, boy,' she said, in a high, cracked voice.

I recognised the woman at once, although I had never before seen her at such close quarters. She was known everywhere as 'La Folle' and in summer could frequently be observed wandering across the fields or down the streets of the village, talking aloud to herself. I had once asked Joseph who she was but he had simply warned me to keep away from her; and even Zoë, normally an inexhaustible store of local knowledge, was uncharacteristically taciturn when I questioned her about the mad lady, although she did vouchsafe that her name was Bernadette and that she lived in a cottage on the edge of the hamlet below the property, behind the house of the gamekeeper, Gaston.

Now that we were face to face I could see her pallid skin and eyes whose colour was so faded that you might for a moment have concluded that she was blind. She appeared to be in her fifties and would have been quite handsome were it not for her expressionless features, which covered her face like a mask.

She took a step towards me but made no effort to put out her hand. 'Come with me, I have something to show you,' she said, reverting this time to French. It sounded like an instruction rather than an invitation.

I hesitated, mindful of Joseph's strictures and uncertain where she wanted to take me. Looking down at Mardi for reassurance, I was somewhat encouraged when she went forward wagging her tail, and sniffed in a friendly way at Bernadette's feet.

Without waiting further Bernadette turned about and moved back down the path, followed by Mardi and myself. We must have looked a curious trio as, one behind the other, we walked through the fields to the road which ran down to the little group of houses. As we passed them I half expected someone to emerge from a door, or open a window and ask me accusingly what I was doing with 'La Folle', but it was a somnolent time of day and no one stirred. Bernadette strode ahead without looking back, carrying an old bag from which emerged a profusion of grasses and wild flowers that she had been gathering on her walk.

When Gaston's brick house came into sight I wondered whether it would not be prudent to seek his protection by knocking on the door; but the shutters were tightly closed and I reflected that he must either be out or resting, in which case he would not welcome any disturbance. So I had no choice but to follow Bernadette to the rear where a tiny cottage, almost a shed, stood behind an overgrown hedge, virtually concealed by bushes and long grass. A once green door, the paint now dark and peeling, was half-open, and the little windows were covered in grime.

Bernadette paused on the threshold and turned to beckon me inside. The room was dark but my eyes quickly adjusted to the gloom and I saw that it was crammed with furniture, much of it broken, across which lay a mass of old clothes in great confusion. She swept some garments from a chair and from a table next to it, and with a gesture invited me to sit down. I wondered why she had remained so silent: perhaps she was still uncertain about my knowledge of French, I thought, or maybe she was trying to summon up a few more words of English. But once I was seated, she vanished through a door into the neighbouring room, reappearing some moments later with a bundle of envelopes which she clutched together with both hands. She too then sat although she made no move to take off her hat or signify in any other way that she was now in her own house.

After some fumbling, a piece of paper almost falling apart at the folds was thrust across the table in my direction. It was yellowing, but a regimental crest was clearly visible at the top and I had little difficulty in reading the handwriting. The message was brief, and in English: 'I and my brother officer wish to offer you our sincerest condolences on the death of your sister. We deeply regret the terrible accident which over-took her. As we leave for the line we shall remember how well poor Albertine looked after us.' The signature was illegible, but was dated May 1915.

I looked up bewildered to find Bernadette staring at me. She was breathing heavily. 'Those men, they took her away,' she exclaimed hoarsely. 'But she came back . . . she still walks in the house . . . You are English, you can find her for me.'

Before I could decide how to respond, I heard footsteps outside and Joseph stood framed in the doorway. He peered into the room and then beckoned to me abruptly to come out to him in the courtyard: 'I saw you following her,' he said crossly as I emerged into the light. 'Didn't I tell you to keep away: she'll fill your head with I don't know what rubbish. Mademoiselle Yvonne would not be pleased to know that you were here. We had best go straight away back to the house.'

I still had the note in my hand. Telling Joseph to wait I slipped back to Bernadette. She had remained seated, scarcely moving after Joseph's sudden incursion. Now she looked fixedly at me as I put the worn fragment of paper back on the table. 'I will be waiting,' she said tonelessly, but there was no menace in her voice.

We made our way up the road and through the main gateway. Never a loquacious man, Joseph said virtually nothing until we had reached the drive and were heading for the stables where it was time for him to feed Lise's rabbits.

'Well, what did she want then?' Suddenly his curiosity appeared to get the better of him, and he turned abruptly to face me at the entrance to the courtyard.

'Tell me who Albertine was,' I responded indirectly: I was

beginning to learn that information was a commodity in which you could usefully trade.

Joseph's head came forward as if, like a tortoise, he was poking it out from under a shell, and he gave me a hard look. 'So that's it,' he grunted, and then after a pause he added reluctantly: 'You'd better come upstairs.'

Joseph's quarters were above the garage; he had moved there after the death of his wife the previous year. A door in the courtyard opened on to a narrow, wooden staircase which led up to a corridor serving three modest rooms under the roof. They were small and could be hot in summer, but for Joseph they were strategically placed between the kitchen and the gardens where he mostly worked, and they appeared to suit him well enough. I followed him through his little kitchen and sat on the arm of a large, shabby sofa while he stood at the window and looked carefully down at the courtyard below.

'Albertine was her elder sister,' he said at length. 'She was the pretty one and worked in the house with Suzanne and the other maids, while young Bernadette had a place in a café up in the village. There were English officers living in the house and men camping in the grounds. We never discovered exactly what happened: she fell from one of the second-floor windows. There's a cross cut in a stone where she struck the terrace.'

There was a long silence and I thought Joseph had no more to say. He moved uneasily round the little room and pulled at his left ear, a habit of his whenever he felt uncomfortable.

Then he came up close to me: there was an unpleasant mixture of garlic and beer on his breath.

'Fact is,' he said, 'there were a couple of soldiers up there at the time: they were the officers' batmen. She was always fooling about with them. They swore that they were in another room when she fell, and no one could say the contrary. But some of us thought different. Mademoiselle Yvonne was really upset: it was her house and she felt personally responsible. But they all left soon after and the affair was, well, let's say kept quiet. Except that Bernadette never forgot. When she went strange she kept repeating that the English soldiers had done in her sister. Isn't that what she told you?' He looked at me expectantly.

'In a way,' I replied noncommittally. I did not feel like telling him about the note. 'But she also said something about Albertine still being in the house. What did she mean?' I asked.

He stared away from me, embarrassed. 'Some nonsense of hers. No need to talk about that. Now you can help me with the grass.' Clearly he wanted to bring the conversation to an end.

It was early evening and the sun's rays were by now filtering through the tall trees which stood to the west between the plain and the house. After we had distributed fresh grass from a wheelbarrow to the rabbits' cages, I remembered what Joseph had said about a cross on the terrace. I walked slowly down the gravel keeping my eyes fixed on the narrow pavement of stone which ran along the bottom of the house wall. Some of the paving was covered with dirt and I scuffed at it with my shoes before, half-way along the façade, stumbling on a small cross carved in the stone. I looked up to see from which of the top windows the maid had fallen, and found that I was staring at my own room. As the implication dawned on me, a voice behind me said softly: 'That's right. That's where she fell.'

I looked round and saw Thérèse sitting on a bench under one of the trees on the sloping lawn. Its hanging branches, which nearly touched the ground in some places, had shielded her from me. Thérèse had as usual been gardening, and her basket with its little forks, trowels and clippers lay at her feet beside a pile of weeds and dead flowers. She had taken off her straw hat, which she held in her lap while she rested.

I went across the grass and sat down next to her, feeling as if I had been caught doing something wrong. Perhaps it was for this reason that before she could question me, I hastened to tell her about my encounter with Bernadette, the letter she had shown me and what Joseph had told me. Thérèse did not interrupt: she sat quite calmly but listening intently, and frowning a little in thought rather than disapproval.

When I had finished she said: 'I remember quite well how upset everyone was at the time. Yvonne was never sure whether Albertine had been alone when she fell. Of course there had to be an enquiry, but in the end neither of the two soldiers who were on the same floor was accused of anything improper. That did not stop a lot of gossip, some of which reached the ears of Bernadette: poor girl, she was always a little strange, but Albertine's death sent her over the edge.

'She did not attend the burial: she was working away from the village when Albertine died, and we were able to find her and give her the news only after the funeral had taken place. That seems strange now, but there were soldiers occupying the roads and the villages everywhere and communications were difficult. She must have been shown her sister's grave later, but I am not sure that by then she really understood that Albertine was lying there. I did not know, incidentally, that one of the officers had written to her: how extraordinary that the letter should have survived all these years.'

I asked her the same question as I had Joseph: 'Bernadette said her sister was still in the house. What did she mean, Tante Thérèse?'

Thérèse stirred uneasily. 'It's all nonsense,' she replied, using the same phrase as Joseph. 'The servants liked to say that she had been seen on the stairs after her death. But as far as we in the family were concerned that was just their vivid imagination. Houses in France do not shelter ghosts like castles in Scotland! If Albertine still lives I fear it can only be in the head of poor Bernadette.'

She bent down for her basket while I turned to gaze again at my open window on the top floor.

'Did she really fall from my room?' I asked her.

'I think so; but you must not give it another thought. And let me give you a little advice: this affair is better not discussed with Yvonne. For years she had known that those windows on the top floor were dangerous, but she had never got round to having them protected. Afterwards she blamed herself repeat-

edly for what she saw as her negligence: and she felt wounded
that as a result such a tragedy should have happened in her
own house. But it was all very long ago, nearly forty years after
all, and every family should know when to let the past look
after the past.'

We walked across the lawn to an old greenhouse where the
gardening tools were kept. The grass had been freshly cut, and
swallows were diving and swooping low as they hunted for
flying insects. As she opened the glass door, Thérèse said,
'You have nonetheless reminded me that I really should do
something to tidy up Albertine's grave. It lies in the churchyard
just below here but it has been sadly neglected for years.'

In deep thought, I took a roundabout route back to my
room, one which would avoid my meeting Tante Yvonne:
direct from the terrace into the dining-room, where the long
table was already laid for dinner, through the empty salon and
the library, and up a spiral staircase to the rear of the house
which these days was used only by the children or their
nannies. It was the hour before dinner when the children,
emerging from their supper, ran wild over the house or
besieged one of the aunts for a bedtime story. I could hear
them shouting and racing up and down the corridors.

Shutting my door, I sat for a moment on the bed, looking
round the little room, with its faded green wallpaper. The
evening air was full of the sound of starlings chattering on the
roof immediately above me. My eye was inevitably drawn to
the single large window whose sill was barely a foot above the
floor: through it I could almost touch the top branches of the

beech tree under which Thérèse and I had been sitting. I went over to the sill and looked down: the gravel seemed a long way below. For the first time I was conscious of an iron bar, waist high, which connected the two sides of the casement. I wondered whether this had also been my grandfather's room and regretted not having asked Thérèse; but I reflected that she might not know, or might in any case be unwilling to say.

I thought again about Bernadette. 'I'll be waiting,' she had said. The need to do something to help put her mind at greater rest weighed on me. Then I had an idea.

Early the next morning I took Thérèse's gardening basket and slipped away to the little church which, surrounded by some houses and a single grocery shop, lay at the foot of the property. I had walked past it only the previous day when Joseph had escorted me back to the house. The adjacent churchyard harboured a collection of strangely contrasting graves: some boasted ornate, gothic statues, while others were crowned with no more than simple headstones. Although the cemetery was small, it took me some time to find Albertine. Her grave lay in one corner and was marked only by a horizontal rectangular stone on which the legend 'Albertine 1895–1915' could just be made out. Weeds had pushed through the square of gravel in which the gravestone was set, and the stone itself needed cleaning.

I set to work and within an hour had weeded and tidied the grave. It looked, I thought proudly, immaculate compared to its abandoned neighbours. Occasionally I glanced nervously round the churchyard, hoping that I would not be seen, still less disturbed by someone I knew, but none of the villagers who passed occasionally in the distance, including at one moment the trim figure of Suzanne, seemed to notice me. When at length I stood up, my eye fell on a large bunch of carnations which had been placed in a stone vase in front of a prosperous-looking marble obelisk nearby. Yielding to temptation I abstracted a number of the blooms and laid them on Albertine's tombstone. They would not stay fresh for long in the heat, but long enough, I hoped, for my purpose.

Now I had reached the more difficult stage of my mission: I had to find Bernadette and persuade her to return here with me. Knowing her wandering habits, the chances of finding her at home struck me as slim, but it was still early in the day and her cottage was no more than ten minutes' walk so I felt I must take my chance.

I was in luck. As I came through the hedge, I could hear Bernadette talking to herself in the cottage. The door was as before half open; I tapped on it and waited. Her voice fell silent – then she appeared, carrying a large bucket of water. She wore the same hat and dress, and I wondered whether she had removed either since I had left her yesterday. I could see that she recognised me but her expression had the same unsmiling rigidity as before.

I stood squarely in front of her, my hands on my hips. 'Bernadette, I have something to show you: will you come with me? It is not far.' Just as she had done I tried to make this an instruction rather than a request, but I felt nervous and my voice trembled more than I would have wished.

She did not move and I was not sure that she had understood me. I took a few steps away and tried again. 'Come,' I said, as if I was calling to Mardi. This time she put down the pail and began to follow me. Once again we walked in single file, but now I was in the lead. I could feel the sun on my back as we headed up the road. When we reached the entrance to the churchyard Bernadette hesitated and for a moment I thought she would refuse to enter. Fortunately no one appeared to distract her and as I threaded my way through the headstones and monuments I could hear her steps behind me. When we reached Albertine's grave she showed at first no sign of recognition. Had I, I wondered, after all wasted my time or worse courted the displeasure of Tante Thérèse through what she would see as my interference?

I pointed to the gravestone and looked Bernadette in the eyes. 'There, it's Albertine. You see, I have found her again for you. The English soldiers never took her away. Nor does she walk in the house. She is here and you can come whenever you want.'

Bernadette was now looking down at the grave. Still she said nothing; then she bent over and picked up two of the already wilting carnations I had placed there. For the first time she spoke: 'I'll be back soon,' she muttered. She paused and I thought for a moment that she might be going to thank me. But instead she turned away and, an erect figure, walked slowly out of the churchyard. Over the wall I could just see the crown of her hat as she moved down the road.

I collected the basket and hurried back to the house,

resolved to say nothing to Thérèse about what I had done, still less to Tante Yvonne. Then I realised that if Thérèse decided to carry out her intention of tending the grave she would find the work already done and suspect me of having been there before her. It seemed better to take the bull by the horns, and before lunch I caught Thérèse by the door of the salon.

'I did some gardening for you this morning, Tante Thérèse: I have been to the churchyard and tidied the grave. And I showed Bernadette what I had done.' I spoke in a low voice, but at the same time tried to sound casual. Mathilde, however, who had sharp ears, overheard me.

'What's that? Whose grave?' she enquired busily. 'Just our little secret,' replied Thérèse quickly, looking keenly at me. 'How kind of you to save me a journey. And if I am right I think you may have tidied up a little more than a grave.'

## XI Gaston

For days the harvest had been in full swing, the air thick with the hum of tractors and the rattle of mechanical harvesters. Now the work was almost finished, with sheaves of corn standing in stooks in the fields, and hay being trundled in carts to the barns. One afternoon, as I was sitting having tea with Tante Yvonne, Serge called, seeking her assent to the annual shoot which took place over her land. Permission was readily given, but with the stipulation that, Serge told me, Yvonne repeated every year: 'No shooting near the house; I don't like the noise, and anyway we had too much of that during the war.'

Invited by Serge I set off with him to find Gaston who lived not far from Suzanne in the cluster of houses lying just below the property. I had come across the gamekeeper when roaming in the woods or over the plain. Still a young man, in his mid-thirties, he looked older than his years: prematurely balding, he was taciturn not to say melancholic, his temperament possibly affected by the loss of three fingers on his left hand.

It was Florence who told me Gaston's story. Her parents had lived near his family farm and she had known him when he was a child. He had grown up expecting to inherit the farm but his father and uncles had been rival claimants to the land and in the end parcels of fields had been divided among them, scarcely enough to make a living. Then, in 1940, Gaston had been conscripted into the army, only to find himself one of the forty thousand French soldiers taken prisoner at Dunkirk. After the Armistice in June, he believed he would be released but instead, like many of his comrades, he was forced to march eastwards until he reached a Stalag in Germany, where he was assigned to a work Kommando. Ill-treated and half-starved, he accepted (as did many others) an offer to become a civilian worker and was sent to a farm in East Prussia where conditions were little better, and he badly injured his hand.

Promises that most French prisoners would be freed were never honoured, and it was only in 1945 that Gaston was able to make a slow return home by train and on foot. He found that both his parents had died and cousins were now installed at the farm. Labourer's work was in any case now ruled out for him, and it was Florence who persuaded Yvonne to recruit him as a gamekeeper, although in truth there was little game to preserve; and to rent him the cottage where he now lived with his wife, the plump and bubbly Annette, and their young son. Gaston knew every centimetre of Yvonne's land, acting as a kind of unofficial agent with the tenant farmers. With his quiet manner he was well liked by them in his not always easy role, insisting on repairs where necessary, and preserving his mistress's shooting rights from the farmers' sons who were always tempted to poach.

The door of the cottage was opened by a five-year-old boy with curly hair and solemn eyes; his hand was on the collar of a gun dog which was almost as tall as him. The dog gave us a cautious sniff, then returned to its basket under a staircase; the boy soundlessly vanished behind a sofa. Annette welcomed us with laughter and a wide smile, her face as round and ruddy as an apple. She at once placed a coffee pot and some mugs on the table and drew up some chairs for us. It was a friendly room, with a floor of patterned tiles, a wide fireplace and two comfortable chairs at the far end; there was a kitchen stove and a dresser with decorated plates in one corner, and a long table at which we were now seated. The windows allowed in little light, designed as they were to keep out the heat in summer and the cold in winter. It was through one of these that Annette now thrust her head and cheerfully announced our arrival to Gaston who was watering his vegetables at the back of the cottage.

Serge and Gaston sat at the table reviewing the guest list for Sunday's shoot. It included the village doctor, some acquaintances from the local market town, and a number of neighbouring farmers whose land was included in the day – twenty guns in all. Gaston then sketched a plan of the shoot which apparently followed the same pattern every year, the guns being positioned in a rough circle two kilometres in diameter across the plain, moving slowly inwards, shrinking the circle and driving the game before them. He then jotted down the different starting points by numbering slips of paper which would be drawn by lot to avoid any suspicion of favouritism. He was adept, I noticed, at concealing the injured side of his left hand.

'Let's drink to a good day,' he said, opening a cupboard door and bringing out a bottle of *floc*, a sweet liquid much favoured locally as an aperitif. 'I have put up plenty of partridge in the beetroot, and I think there are woodcock in the trees behind Bommaert's farm. We could do with a breeze, though – it gets the birds flying well.' He seemed more animated than usual and I felt that this occasion was one where he took pleasure in demonstrating his skills. 'Now where shall we post the young man?' he added, turning to Serge. After some discussion it was agreed that as Gaston roved round the circle, controlling the speed of its advance, I would see most by walking with him.

Sunday dawned cloudy, but there was enough wind to clear the skies and the promise of a warm, late August day as we met at nine outside Gaston's cottage. There was a buzz of suppressed excitement as the guests arrived, unpacking guns and cartridges from the back of their small Renaults and Citroëns, and allowing their dogs to race up and down the road. They appeared in an assortment of clothes: the doctor sported formal shooting wear in the shape of a tweed jacket and plus fours with thick woollen stockings and a jaunty hat with a pheasant feather. The others mostly contented themselves with loose denim jackets and trousers, and cloth caps. Here and there a pipe was already lit as hands were shaken and, in my case, introductions made.

Serge clapped his hands and the slips of paper with the starting positions were drawn, with an instruction to begin the shoot in precisely half an hour. Serge took one group away to begin walking at the edge of the woods below his house on the far side of the plain. Gaston and a number of the farmers strung themselves along fields of beetroot and stubble, each having his neighbour just in sight. Then we paused, standing quietly while waiting for the village clock to strike the hour.

The faintest of breezes, blowing directly towards us, kept us cool as we stood in the sun, while all around us larks were calling, filling the air with their shrill twittering. Gaston, a whistle on a cord round his neck, his gun broken under his arm, lit a cigarette. 'Next time,' he said, 'you too can have a gun. But you need to know what to do to avoid accidents, especially later when we close the circle, so watch carefully. It can be exciting at the end and Monsieur Serge only invites people who can be relied on to keep their heads. Is this how you do it in your country?'

This was the longest exchange I had so far managed with Gaston. I replied that I thought our shoots were usually organised in drives with beaters. 'Of course that's also how it is mostly done here,' he said, 'but I prefer our rough shooting. It is better sport than what the gentry like, waiting for birds to be forced over their heads, especially those fat pheasants that fly like geese.' Just then the clock above us began to strike and Gaston blew his whistle. A cry was taken up along the line and we began to walk slowly into the first field. A hare rose some way from us, paused, its ears erect, and then leapt forwards in long bounds. 'One for later,' remarked Gaston. Far to our right, a covey of partridge flew along the line and I could hear a volley of shots as they passed each gun.

For the next two hours we tramped laboriously through what seemed endless expanses of beet and kale, the damp leaves dragging at our legs, with our progress occasionally enlivened by a hare or rabbit rising under our feet, or a startled bird, often a lark or a snipe, taking off beside us. Gaston refrained in general from shooting, except as a bird or hare sought to run back past us, when he rarely missed. The partridge rose mostly far off, but he said the game would nonetheless be ours, as we would discover soon enough in the afternoon. From time to time we would walk sideways behind the guns to ensure that they were holding to the circle, Serge apparently performing the same office in the distance. Then at midday the guns on our side of the ring moved towards a stand of trees, where some logs had been placed in the form of rough benches and we found bread, sausage, fruit and a case of beer which had been left there by Annette. Each of my companions had his story of triumphs or near misses as he pulled game out of his bag and handed it to Gaston. The dogs, their sides heaving and tongues hanging, flopped down in the shade waiting for water to be brought to them by their masters from a barrel thoughtfully placed behind the benches.

After we had rested, Gaston stood and addressed us. 'Messieurs, here we come to the serious part of the day. Please remember that our circle is now no more than seven hundred metres across so you must shoot either high or low. There will be plenty of game so you will bear in mind at all times the safety not only of your neighbour but of those in front of you, even if you do not see them. And remember, when you hear my whistle, all shooting must stop. Good luck, Messieurs, to your posts: we start walking again in exactly fifteen minutes.' As we separated, I noticed a number of the guests donning plastic spectacles. Gaston told me this was a sensible precaution. 'We have never had an accident here,' he remarked grimly, 'but I have heard of many similar occasions where people have had their sight damaged or an eye lost.'

Settling his cap low over his eyes, he instructed me to stay by the trees while he went to ensure that the guns had taken up their correct positions. I sat down on a log and idly looked around me. My eye fell on a tuft of grass where one of the guests had left a drinking bowl for his dog. I picked it up together with a round piece of discoloured metal which I put without thinking into my pocket. On his return Gaston took me to the far side of the wood, where we waited for the line to pass us before following at a careful distance behind.

Before long, led by Serge's tall figure, the guns came into

view over the flat horizon. It was early afternoon and the sun was high above us. Then, as we advanced, coveys of partridge rose and began to swoop both towards and away from us. Ten minutes later, and flocks of them were breaking out of the cauldron we had created, five or six in each flock falling to the guns who were now no more than a hundred metres apart. As the circle shrank still further, the wildlife on the ground also sought to escape, tens of hares running past us so that it became hard to decide whether to aim at the birds or at the game at one's feet. Gaston too now shot without restraint, turning his back to the circle and unerringly bringing surviving birds down from behind. Last to show themselves were the rabbits, which at first hid under leaves and wheat stalks, but were then also forced to break cover. At last, as shot from the guns facing us began to rustle overhead, Gaston blew his whistle and all firing stopped. Silence fell on us like a blanket, our ears still ringing from this last round of continuous firing.

As we all walked the last few paces towards each other, the dogs, now let off their leashes, ran back and forth, noses to the ground, picking up the game and bringing it to their masters. We gathered it together and then started on the trek up the gradual incline from the plain back to Gaston's cottage. As we went, I fell in with the doctor who had clearly enjoyed himself and was anxious to impress me with the size of his bag. I gathered that he found the village practice rather beneath his talents, only remaining in the area because of his passion for rural life. His bucolic enthusiasm had clearly survived the daily experience of treating farmers and their families, often in conditions of ignorance and squalor. I could almost hear a sardonic laugh from Tante Yvonne as he expanded on his lyrical view of country life.

When we reached the cottage we were greeted by the smell of cooking. A long table on trestles had been set up on a patch of grass in front of the house. Gaston busied himself laying out the *tableau de chasse*: there were more than a hundred partridge, interspersed with the occasional snipe or woodcock, which he arranged in concentric circles, and two long rows of hares. After admiring the bag, we rested under the trees behind the cottage, until Gaston and Annette emerged bearing heavy cooking pots of game stew which we fell on with relish. As glasses of beer or rough red wine were emptied, the talk along the table became louder and more convivial, and tales of shooting exploits ever less credible. No one noticed that a car had halted in the road outside until a red-faced elderly man with greying hair walked through the gate and up the path. His manner seemed to me to be uncertain but at the same time defiant.

It was Gaston's reaction which brought conversation to a halt. The moment he caught sight of our visitor he jumped to his feet, pale with evident anger, while Annette, who had been distributing more plates round the table, silently disappeared inside. Advancing from the end of the table, Gaston seemed barely able to speak: 'You . . . You . . . You were told never to set foot here . . .' But the man seemed set on ignoring Gaston's rage. 'Come now,' he blustered, with a forced smile and swaying slightly on his feet, 'you are having a party. Will you not offer me a drink with your friends? Where is our Annette?'

Gaston raised an arm as if to strike him and might indeed have done so had not Serge intervened. He moved swiftly from the table, took the new arrival by the shoulder, and marched him slowly but firmly back through the gate. Once in the road, Serge exchanged a few words with him and moments later we heard the car drive off. He then resumed his seat and the conversation picked up again as if nothing untoward had occurred. Gaston, having found Annette, also came back to his chair, but he remained noticeably subdued for the rest of the evening. No reference was made to the visitor, and although I sensed that most people had, with some embarrassment, recognised him, I thought it better not to enquire who he was until later.

Dusk was beginning to fall earlier now, and although the evening was still light, there was a crescent moon in the sky as we separated, the game having been distributed among the guests. The consensus was that it had been a good day and Gaston seemed cheered by the compliments he received as well as, no doubt, by the notes that were thrust into his hand. Serge handed me several partridge for Tante Yvonne, and offered to bring some of the other game up to the house. Once we were in the meadow, I asked him the meaning of the scene we had witnessed.

Serge hesitated before replying, and at first would only say that there were good reasons for Gaston's conduct. We were approaching the wooden bench by the former tennis court where I would sometimes rest with Auguste during our walks, and when I pressed him at least to tell me who the stranger was, he sat down rather heavily.

'Alright,' he said reluctantly, and after another pause, 'it is a not uncommon story in the country, I fear, and although most of our friends are in the know they never mention it – nor should you. Gaston was already "walking out" with Annette when he was conscripted – he adored her but lost all contact with her for the five years he was in Germany. When he returned she was still living at home, not married. But she was pregnant, and what was worse, pregnant by her father's brother. Who knows whether the man forced himself on her or seduced her.

'Normally when an illegitimate child is born around here, it is given away for adoption, the more so where there is a suspicion of incest. But Gaston was determined to have Annette, and he has acknowledged the boy as his own. You saw Jeannot. A fine lad he is too. The unspoken condition was that the family would keep quiet and Annette's uncle would stay well away from her. I don't know what possessed him to show up today. Perhaps it was drink – he and his brother always hit the bottle on Sundays. I warned him that there could be violence if he showed his face there again, so I just hope he has listened to me.'

Confused and dismayed by these revelations about what seemed outwardly so normal and happy a couple, I asked about Annette. 'She has been a good wife to him,' said Serge. 'Of course she was grateful to Gaston but she loves him and does her best to make him happy. It is sad that they have no other children, but it is not yet too late for them.

'So you have learnt something more today about the customs of the countryside,' he added, adjusting the game bag on his shoulder and looking down at me with his slow smile, while sensing perhaps my perplexity. 'Florence knows the story well and will help you understand how these things can happen. You may talk to her, but tell her I asked you not to speak to anyone else. Florence has been a good friend to Gaston and his family, and I only hope she can advise him and Annette about what, if anything, they should say to Jeannot about his parentage when he's older. It will not be easy for them.'

We reached the house and entered the kitchen by the side door, depositing the game on slate shelves in a larder at the back. Zoë was gone and the kitchen was deserted. As I emptied my pockets I found the metal disc I had picked up at midday, and handed it to Serge. He was at once interested, taking it under a lamp and rubbing the metal with a cloth. Some numbers appeared, and turning to me he exclaimed: 'This is important. It is an English soldier's identity disc – every man in your army wore one. You will need to show me the exact spot you found it, and I must take it to the gendarmerie. They will want to make sure there is nothing else left there, then they will send it away for identification. And you must be sure to ask who the disc belonged to.

'Much of the plain was a battlefield on the retreat to Dunkirk,' he added. 'Only ten years ago, where we were shooting birds today, men were shooting at each other. Let's hope that in another ten years we will still only be aiming at partridges.'

## XII  Monsieur Bertrand

One of Florence's regular duties was to collect a supply of flour
for use in the kitchen from a mill on the far side of the village.
Madeleine would drive her the short distance round the foot of
the village to the old windmill, an excursion which Florence
enjoyed treating as a social call: an opportunity to catch up on
the local farm gossip as well as on news of the miller's extended
family. For me, crammed one late August afternoon into the
back of the rocking and whining little Citroën, this expedition
presented the opportunity to explore another country, the
plain below the house being by now familiar territory.

The arms of the mill, covered by discoloured and flapping

sailcloth, were slowly turning as we drove up a rise and then into a dusty courtyard; the regular thud of a diesel engine showed that on this very calm day the mill needed the assistance of more than wind power for its operation. It was a circular, wooden slatted structure, sitting on a brick foundation, dominated by its gigantic sails and attached to great levers with which it could be ratcheted round into the wind. The miller's bespectacled face, surmounted by the usual grubby cloth cap, was framed for a moment in an upper window before he clattered down a staircase in his wooden clogs to greet us. On arrival he looked to me as large and round as his mill; while his wife, following close behind, almost rivalled him in size, her huge girth and pendulous bosom precariously covered by a threadbare black dress. 'It's all that flour which makes them swell up,' said Florence to me later.

Florence and Madeleine were invited into a long, low cottage which stretched down one side of the courtyard, while the miller asked me to help him carry sacks of flour to the back of the car. 'Now you be sure to remember me to Mademoiselle Yvonne,' he gasped, catching his breath between loads. 'She saved my livelihood during the war, you know. My main beam – it holds the mill together – split one winter and there was no timber of the size and strength I needed to be found, not at any price. She heard about it and at once offered to have one of her oaks cut and prepared for me. I'll never forget it.'

The rear of the Citroën was by now so weighed down with quantities of flour that I was asking myself how I would fit inside for the return journey, when Florence and Madeleine reappeared. 'Henriètte has just told us that the herons have been gathering. You have to go and see them,' said Florence. 'Their wood is between here and the village, and if you don't mind the walk it will only take an hour or so for you to return home on foot.' They went with me to the courtyard entrance. Through a heat-haze I could see that the surrounding fields were bordered at the far end by a dense clump of trees which sloped up in the distance towards the village walls. 'The heronry is round a pond in the wood,' explained Florence. 'All the paths through the trees lead to it, you cannot miss it,' she added, seeing that I looked hesitant.

I set off, stumbling over furrows of plough, but before long I reached a thicket where a track led me deeper into the trees. Mole's terror in the Wild Wood had made an indelible impression on me when I first read *The Wind in the Willows*, and as a result woods had always given me an ill-defined sense of unease: a fear when alone of losing all sense of direction, of being swallowed up and vanishing without trace. The shelter from the hot sun was welcome, but despite Florence's reassuring words my usual worries surfaced as the path wound its way with no apparent logic or purpose, criss-crossed by other confident-looking tracks made by deer or rabbits, which tempted you to take what appeared to be a more direct course, but which always petered out after several yards. In some places dense thickets of brambles closed in on me, claustrophobic and unwelcoming, in others the path led through glades of tall trees where shafts of sunlight fell through curtains of dancing midges on to the smooth turf.

Just as I was losing all hope of finding the pond I glimpsed through the undergrowth an expanse of water ahead, surrounded by vast beech trees. Looking up through the leaves, I saw what appeared to be great platforms of branches on which sat, hunched and silent, countless grey birds, like old women sheltering under cloaks. I must have been spotted, for on my approach one of the herons rose from its nest and, taking off, lazily circled the trees, its long, thin legs dangling, before returning to its lofty vantage point. I reached the pond and sat for a moment on its bank, watching the ripples made by the rising fish. Then, entranced, I spied on the far side a heron standing in the water, motionless as if carved in stone. For a minute we observed each other until, with what seemed studied indifference, it waded slowly along the water's edge until it reached the shelter of some bushes.

I lay on my back for some time, watching the great noiseless birds, until I became anxious to move on. Florence had said that any path from the pond would take me to the far side of the wood, but the one I chose soon divided and, hoping for the best, I took a right fork. Before long my path broadened into a mossy ride and I began to detect signs that there had in the past been human efforts to tame the wood: bushes had once been shaped and I came across a rotting wooden bench. Down a track, again to the right, I thought I could see a plinth for a statue and, my curiosity aroused, I took this direction until I came to what might have been a summerhouse, its roof overgrown with wild honeysuckle and a decaying veranda covered in ivy. A few more paces took me through a clump of rhododendrons and I found myself on a stretch of grass leading up to a terrace shaded by three great lime trees. Behind these trees I could just make out what appeared to be a substantial house, built of red brick with a gothick ornamental façade and turrets at each end.

Emboldened by the overall atmosphere of abandonment I walked towards the terrace, where the gravel was now sprouting weeds. But as I neared one of the lime trees I suddenly noticed I was being watched: a man in a straw hat with a wide brim and, despite the heat, a linen jacket and tie was seated under one of the trees from where he had been observing my progress. For a moment I froze, uncertain whether to make a rapid retreat, but then he called out 'Come here, boy' and I went uncertainly forward. I could now see that he was a smartly dressed man in his seventies, with a grey moustache and a careworn face, but his expression was benevolent as he looked me up and down.

'So who are you? What brings you here?' he asked not unkindly. I told him that I had lost my way and was from the big house on the other side of the village. He looked pensive. 'Ah,' he mused, '*la famille qui n'est plus dans la course*'.* He did not elaborate, but motioned me to sit on the bench. After a minute in which he introduced himself as Pierre Bertrand and quickly established that I was English, he suggested we drink tea – 'to remind you of home' – and led me through a side

* The family that has dropped out of the race.

door and into a vast, empty kitchen. He boiled up some water in a saucepan on a little stove fuelled by a gas canister, and tea was made in an old china pot, chipped like the cups he found in a cupboard.

As we sat at a side table, he continued: 'This is not my property, but I come here to keep an eye on it. It is the Deklerk house – have they told you about it?' He eyed me rather anxiously, I thought, and seemed if anything relieved when I shook my head. 'It now belongs to my old friend Paul Deklerk who has not lived here since he lost his wife Agnes at the end of the war. It was a terrible accident – she was found at the foot of the terrace steps, her neck broken. I keep trying to persuade Paul to come back – after all his father and grand-father lived here, but he won't return. So I watch over the place for him. It is an excuse to get out of town, but I cannot stop things falling apart. As you can see, Nature is taking over outside, and as for inside – well, I'll show you.'

I was surprised that he was confiding in me, a stranger and a youthful one at that, and wondered whether he was not rather lonely in his self-imposed task. We moved from the kitchen directly into a long dining-room with mirrors at each end. Glass cabinets were full of porcelain and there were menus written on china stands recording the courses served at lunches or dinners on special occasions long ago. Throwing back shutters as we moved from one room to the next, he lifted dust-sheets to reveal embroidered chairs and sofas, while explaining to me the origins of the pictures, mainly stiff nineteenth-century portraits. Despite the opened shutters, light seemed barely to penetrate these sombre rooms, with their stained wallpaper and by now grimy windows. Everywhere there was the same smell of damp and decay. At the end of the house we came to a library, lined from floor to ceiling with leather-bound books. 'This is where Paul's father wrote; he was one of our best-known historians thirty years ago,' explained Monsieur Bertrand. I would have liked to linger, but he was now in a hurry and pressed on down a corridor where antlers and boars' heads sprouted from the walls.

'Now you will need help returning home,' said Monsieur Bertrand as we emerged into the sunshine, 'it will be a long walk for you and it is getting late. I can drive you to the village – it is on my way – but you will forgive me if I do not take you down to the house. I am not sure that I would be altogether welcome there.' With this enigmatic remark – and something in his manner discouraged questions – he asked me to wait outside while he made the house secure; then he shepherded me into an old car, a replica of the one driven by Joseph, and set off down a drive leading from the far side of the house through iron gates which he carefully pulled together and locked. I noticed graffiti on the pillars, but could not comprehend the letters and symbols.

We drove to the village in silence: Monsieur Bertrand's mood seemed to have darkened although I could not tell why. Eventually, as we reached the square and he brought the car to a halt, he turned to me.

'I have enjoyed your company, young man,' he said (I noticed I had graduated from the earlier 'boy'). 'Please give my respects to Mademoiselle Yvonne. I am tempted to ask you to say to her from Pierre Bertrand that in those war years people were only doing their best. But perhaps not – maybe we should leave the past alone. No doubt you are learning a lot about the recent painful history of our dear country. If I can give you one word of advice: always keep an open mind.'

With these words he lifted his straw boater and accelerated down the street. Puzzled by both his little homily and his demeanour, I took the steep red path that led directly from the village down to the house. Then, as I rounded the drive, I saw Madeleine standing on the front steps. She gave me a wave and I ran across the grass to her, eager to tell her about my unusual afternoon. No sooner had I mentioned Monsieur Bertrand, however, than her welcoming smile was replaced by a worried frown and she beckoned me to the kitchen garden where we could sit and speak alone.

'I entirely forgot when we told you to see the herons that we were also sending you in the direction of the Deklerk house, although it has been deserted for the past five years. I think it better that you don't mention to my mother that you found yourself there or that you met Bertrand.'

She turned to me and took my hand. 'It is so hard for you to understand if your country has never been occupied. Everyone reacted differently to the Germans. Serge went underground and his family suffered badly in consequence. We had to share this house with the military until they threw us out. Neither Tante Yvonne nor Lise have forgotten the indignity. Paul Deklerk's family had always been pro-German

– his father was an expert on German history – and Paul decided it was best to work with them. He was already an official in the local Prefecture and I think he did what he could for everyone, until the SS took over in 1943 and he was increasingly drawn into their activities. Even then he avoided the worst, but he was known as a collaborator and the SS used his place as a headquarters. The Deklerk house has had a sinister reputation ever since.

'I will never forget the day we were told by an SS officer that we had twenty-four hours to leave this house. Much as we hated setting foot there, Tante Yvonne took mother and myself – I was thirteen, but maybe they thought it would help to have me with them – straight to the Deklerks to ask Paul to intercede on our behalf. He and his wife seemed to us to be living in the lap of luxury compared with our own situation, and I could see at once that they weren't going to risk their position with the Germans by lifting a finger to help us. I don't know which was worse, their patronising attitude or the hypocrisy with which Paul said he would see what he could do. One telephone call would have helped, but the next day we were packing and leaving.

'Pierre Bertrand refused to become involved or to work with him,' she went on, 'but he remained the good friend of the Deklerk family he had always been. After the war, when Paul was imprisoned for a time, Bertrand, who is a lawyer, became very unpopular round here through his efforts to prevent the house being confiscated. He has also saved it from being vandalised. But Paul Deklerk will never be able to come back here, and not just because of his wife's accident. Bertrand was careful to tell you only part of the story.

'Quite a lot for you to take in!' She looked gravely out over the little squares of box surrounding the growing vegetables to the curved brick wall with its espaliered fruit trees. 'It was all over several years ago and I try not to think about that unhappy time. It is harder for mother and Tante Yvonne, and also for Serge, but I for one am not going to fight those battles any more. There is so much else in life.'

The bell rang for dinner. Together we moved back along the terrace, where the aunts were sitting, quietly enjoying the setting sun. Their peaceful gathering reminded me for a moment of the herons I had watched that afternoon.

## XIII Madeleine

As August moved into September the time for my departure began to approach, although I resolutely refused to contemplate the day when I would actually have to leave. The days became if anything even warmer. The aunts seemed unmoved by the heat although they could scarcely have been used to such temperatures. Oncle Auguste tapped the barometer in the hall every morning before going out as a precaution against being caught in the rain, but apart from the solitary storm on the day I had lost the statue, the needle had not flickered from fair for weeks.

One day, in the relative cool of a late afternoon, I decided to visit Serge who I knew lived with his mother on the other side of the neighbouring hillside, but whose house I still had not seen. Although the hill was wooded I felt confident for once that in this vicinity I could scarcely lose myself.

I whistled to Mardi and walked down into the fields. Eventually the ground began to slope upwards and I crossed a meadow which bordered the wood; as I climbed a track through the trees, Mardi crashed ahead in the undergrowth. The track joined another path from below, one that had known better days for there were occasionally cracked stone steps and in some places even the remains of a wooden handrail, planted no doubt to assist the less athletic of Serge's forebears to make their way up. The slope was now steep; I pressed on, sensing that the top must be near. Then, just above, I heard Mardi barking and whining, and Serge's voice trying to calm her. As I came out of the trees, I saw Serge, holding hands with Madeleine. They were standing in front of a tall, square tower whose upper portion disappeared through the branches above. Madeleine seemed, I thought, somewhat disconcerted at my unexpected appearance, but Serge came towards me with a broad smile. His height was such that Madeleine seemed in comparison far shorter than she really was; while his wavy brown hair appeared dark in contrast with her pale looks. I felt a fleeting pang of jealousy as I saw the two of them together.

'Welcome,' he said, 'we were on our way to the top. Come and see the view.'

The space round the tower was humid, almost chill, and the

structure itself looked faintly sinister. Perhaps it was the dark jagged stones from which it had been built, or the slits at irregular intervals in the walls, which gave it a menacing aspect.

'Built as a vantage point by my great-grandfather when he bought Grey Hill,' explained Serge as I looked enquiringly upwards.

We climbed up a shaky wooden staircase which was liberally spattered with bird droppings. The place smelt damp and only occasional shafts of light penetrated the gloom until we reached the last flight of steps. But the light and heat struck at us as we came through a door on to a platform. The plain stretched out on all sides, vanishing into the heat-haze, while the hills to our left and right were caught in the setting sun. I could make out the roof of our house below the village walls.

Serge looked round reflectively. 'There could be plenty of pigeons soon. Let's stay for half an hour and see. It can be your turn to try a little shooting now you have seen some for yourself.' He ducked back through the door of the floor below. 'You can use my old 20-bore; I bagged scores of birds with it at your age,' he shouted up the staircase, banging open and shut a cupboard door and reappearing with two shotguns.

'This is where I go down, it's too noisy for me,' said Madeleine firmly. 'I'll find your mother, Serge, and,' she turned to me, 'if you are not too late I will drive you home.' With a wave she was gone.

We leaned over the parapet: there was not a bird in sight. 'It is still a little early for them,' said Serge. 'The sun will be down soon, then the pigeons will be flying in from the plain to rest in these trees.'

We fell silent, gazing at the view. Serge pointed to his right. 'That is where the Germans came from in '40 and', turning to his left, 'that was the line of retreat of you British. I saw a lot of the battle from up here until I joined my parents in Tante Yvonne's cellars. Down!'

He grabbed my arm and pulled me with him below the parapet as a flock of pigeons flashed past us. 'Those ones saw us, but the others will start to come in now.' He cocked his shotgun and loaded mine, showing me how to work the safety catch.

Three more bunches of pigeons appeared, seemingly out of an empty sky, and headed towards us. This time they circled the tower, as if inspecting the trees below. Serge shouldered his gun and fired: there was a cloud of feathers and a bird nose-dived through the trees, hitting the ground below with a thud. I could hear Mardi give a surprised but jubilant bark.

Pigeons were now flying towards us from all directions. Serge fired several times, hitting a bird with each volley. It seemed time to have a go. I raised my gun and aimed blindly at a group of pigeons as they raced by: there was an explosion and the gun jerked upwards as it recoiled into my shoulder.

'Not like that,' said Serge from behind me, 'use your left arm as a cradle, and pick one bird. If you fire into the crowd you will miss. Here they come again!'

Once more several flocks appeared to fly straight at us. This time I swung my arm more deliberately and squeezed the trigger less excitedly.

'Got him!' I cried as the leading bird of a group seemed to pause in mid-flight and then plunge through the trees. My first kill! All at once, as suddenly as they had appeared, the pigeons were gone.

'Keep your eyes open, they will be back,' said Serge, and as he spoke two more flocks flew round the tower, searching for a tree to roost in; others followed in quick succession. Serge continued steadily firing and the birds fell regularly to the ground. I claimed a second hit.

Before long the sun, a fading orange ball, was sinking rapidly behind us. 'We must find our birds before it is too dark,' he declared. 'Let's go down.'

When we reached the ground, Mardi was looking for the game. Although not trained as a gun-dog, she guided us to the birds and we stumbled down through the wood with eight pigeons to our credit. I walked awkwardly with my gun, but insisted on carrying a couple of birds as a symbol of my success. Abruptly the path came to the edge of a steep slope and I was looking down on the roof and courtyard of a substantial house below, built almost into the side of the hill. Minutes later, in stockinged feet, I entered a dark drawing-room and shook hands with a frail elderly lady in a mob cap, Serge's mother.

Madeleine, who was sitting by her, looked on edge. I could sense her taut nerves even before she asked querulously why we had been so long. She insisted that we go without delay, took perfunctory leave of the old lady and almost raced to the car in the courtyard.

Serge, evidently accustomed to these moods, made no real attempt to detain her. He thrust two pigeons into my hand as he shut the tinny door of the car on me, and walked round to embrace Madeleine who was already at the wheel. He stood looking after us as we swayed down the drive.

Madeleine stared fixedly ahead, then gave me a quick glance as we shot through the gates to the road.

'I'm sorry, but I couldn't stay there a moment longer. Let's drive round by the plain.' It was a statement of intent rather than a suggestion. We took a turning too fast, then slowed to a crawl.

'Serge's mother has just asked me when we are going to marry,' Madeleine said suddenly, almost to herself. She was breathing heavily and her shoulders were hunched. 'She told me I could not keep him waiting much longer. If only she knew that every time she pushes me I have more doubts. Serge is too nice, far too kind for me. I feel stifled here – I must get away!'

Her words sent a chill through me. Jealousy of Serge gave way to a sense of gloom, almost despair, at the thought that she might leave the house. First Bob and then Madeleine. I was surprised by how passionately I wanted this world I had so recently discovered to stay intact; her talk of departure felt to me like betrayal.

'No, please stay, you can't leave Tante Yvonne and all of us,' I exclaimed.

For the first time she seemed conscious of me and managed a thin smile.

'I am sorry, I should not be speaking to you like this. But there is no one to talk to; not even mother will listen to me. They all think he is so perfect, they cannot understand why I am hesitating. When he proposed to me nearly two years ago I said "yes, but later" – and now it is later. Serge is too gentle to press me himself, still less get annoyed – if only he could become more angry perhaps that would be better.'

We rounded the hill into the plain, and headed along the narrow road through empty fields. The dusk had turned to dark, and I could see the lights of the house above and ahead of us as the road pointed directly towards the village. A rabbit, caught in our headlights, froze and then at the last moment vanished into a ditch.

'I feel so trapped – by mother who wants me to marry Serge and by Tante Yvonne and the others who depend on me to keep the house in order. How can I go on like this?' she asked rhetorically as we turned into the drive.

That evening, while I crouched over a game board, playing *jacquet* with Tante Yvonne, I told her about my walk and the shoot.

'Serge is a very brave young man,' she said. 'He does not talk about it, but he did wonderful things as a boy during the war. And he and his family paid a terrible price.'

I looked up enquiringly, as she leaned forward in her chair.

'It all began with the tower. He used to go up there and watch the air battles. When your planes were shot down he would search for them and get the pilots back to the house if he could; then he would pass them on to the Resistance. He got away with it for a year or so, but of course it was only a matter of time before the Germans discovered what he was doing. Some soldiers came to find him, but he had been warned that they were searching for him and was hiding in the woods. So they dragged his father, old Alphonse, who was an invalid, up to the tower and they shot him there. It was Serge who found him a few hours later. Someone had betrayed him; I have my own ideas about who it was, but I have always kept them to myself. There were too many witch-hunts in this country after the war.'

I stared down at the board, trying to keep my composure by counting the black and white spaces.

'His mother has never really recovered. She more or less ran the two farms until Serge was old enough to take them over. All she wants now is for him to marry and have a family – and of course we too would like him to do that,' added Yvonne with a slow smile.

I was still brooding on Madeleine's outburst to me when an unexpected arrival, only a few days after our visit to Grey Hill, brought matters to a head.

It was four in the afternoon. Much of the plain was once again obscured by the heat and I was lying under a lime tree at the front of the house, where it was cooler, repairing a child's bicycle. Music drifted down from a fair in the village: a single refrain was being played again and again through loud-speakers standing round the stalls on the main square. A whirring noise in the old stables told me that Tante Florence was extracting honey from her beehives; while with a monstrous clattering in the kitchen Lise was replenishing the stove, removing the heavy iron circles in order to pour in the coals. Tante Yvonne called this noisy daily ritual the '*bal des ronds*'.*

The little Citroën turned into the drive, passed under a perilously leaning oak tree and, with its engine's familiar whine, came to a stop at the front steps. From the shadows of my retreat I saw a blond young man emerge, look up at the house and somewhat hesitantly press the bell. The door was opened and he vanished inside.

The first hint that anything unusual was happening was the appearance of Zoë, flustered and almost running from the kitchen to the stables.

'Come quickly,' she called to Tante Florence. 'There is a German with Mademoiselle Yvonne.' Florence emerged, her face protected by a veil of muslin and wearing heavy gardening gloves.

'Calm down, he won't eat her I suppose,' she replied cheerfully, climbing the back steps to the door of the pantry.

Ten minutes later Zoë was back, this time looking for me.

'Mademoiselle Yvonne wants you to come to the drawing-room,' she said, as if conveying a royal command, 'and I am to make tea,' she added doubtfully.

The atmosphere as I entered the small salon was clearly strained. Tante Yvonne, a shapeless mass in purple, her face

---

* The dance of the rings.

nscrutable, sat in her usual armchair behind the round table at the window. The visitor was perched awkwardly in front of her, on a rickety gilt chair whose back I knew was liable to come apart at the seat if you moved too suddenly. Florence, also by the window, had taken out her sewing and appeared intent on her stitches. Tante Alice was busily and unnecessarily positioning small tables round the room. Madeleine stood, looking a little flushed, by the fireplace. No one was speaking.

My arrival broke the silence.

'Our German friend,' said Tante Yvonne drily by way of introduction, 'billeted here during the war. He wanted to pay us a visit.' We shook hands; he was quite short, with very pale, almost transparent blue eyes, and fair hair which despite his evident youth was already receding.

'Otto Schmidt,' he said, 'lecturer at Cologne University,' and felt constrained to repeat to me what he had evidently already recalled to the others. 'My regiment was transferred from here straight to the Russian front. We were stationed in the village for two years and I never forgot this house and how correct and', he hesitated, *'polite'* – I felt he wanted to say 'kind' – 'you all were. I have not found it easy as a German to visit France, even six years after the war, but I had the chance to travel this summer and I felt the need to return.' He was, I thought, appealing to us all to agree with him.

'Now tell us about Cologne,' said Florence as Zoë hobbled in disapprovingly with the tea-tray. Otto responded gratefully with an account of the university where he specialised in economics. He spoke grammatical if rather stilted French.

Madeleine and her three aunts listened impassively: only Florence kept him going with questions and comments. Although he rarely looked at her, I sensed that Otto was seeking to engage Madeleine's attention. Her only response was to stare fixedly out of the window.

Eventually Otto vouchsafed that he was spending two days in the village, having found a room there.

'If I may I would like to walk once in your property,' he said timidly. Tante Yvonne smiled for the first time.

'You are welcome to do so. You may find fewer trees than when you left, thanks to the exertions of your countrymen, otherwise not so much has changed. If you would like a walk now, I am sure Madeleine will accompany you.' Madeleine was I thought going to protest, but instead she too managed to smile.

'I should be pleased to show you round,' she said.

I went with Otto and Madeleine as far as the white wooden gates which led across the road and down to the lake. It was still very warm and the sun quite high, but Otto showed no disposition to remove the jacket and tie he had put on for his call. We walked first along the terrace, then down the path through the long grass in the meadow. Otto looked round him like a man in a dream, obviously torn between a desire to point out places and incidents he remembered from the past, and a fear of giving offence to Madeleine. He need not have worried. With every step Madeleine was becoming more animated and friendly. Soon they were even recalling the forced move of Yvonne and Lise to the village over which Otto and his fellow officers had done their best to be helpful before they, too, had left. As I turned away the two of them were deep in conversation; it suddenly occurred to me that Otto might have risked the embarrassment of this return for rather more than a renewed acquaintance with the polite family he professed to remember.

Otto's car moved back down the drive just as Tante Yvonne led the way into the dining-room for dinner. Madeleine slipped a little furtively into the room and found her place at one end of the table.

Tante Alice wasted no time in opening fire.

'Well, how insensitive and how German! Yvonne, you were much too nice to that young man. I would have shown him the door.' Her little eyes glinted, while her white curls shook and she bared her gold tooth.

'I have never broken the laws of hospitality in this house,' replied Tante Yvonne, 'except perhaps in wartime, and the war is after all long over.'

'I found him most interesting. I always wanted to visit Cologne,' remarked Florence placidly.

Oncle Auguste appeared not to have been following the conversation, but he suddenly lifted his head from his soup. 'The Boches, the Boches . . .' he began. His voice trailed away.

'Quite right, Auguste,' said Tante Alice firmly.

Madeleine leaned forward and shot a defiant glance round the table. 'Tante Yvonne, I have asked Otto Schmidt to have lunch with us tomorrow. I felt sure you would agree.' Her voice trembled just a little.

Total silence followed this announcement. I looked anxiously at Oncle Auguste, expecting some vigorous reaction, but to my surprise he continued, apparently unconcerned, to slop soup into his mouth. Tante Alice appeared stunned and Florence looked worried; Tante Thérèse seemed on the edge of tears. But before Tante Yvonne could respond Mathilde jumped in.

'Good idea,' she said briskly, 'then we can all have a look at him.'

Finally Yvonne spoke. 'I only hope that everyone', she said quietly, 'will remember he is our guest.'

If Tante Yvonne was concerned or irritated by Madeleine's invitation, she did not show it. She did not revert to the subject that evening, nor did Madeleine apparently feel the need to make any further comment, or to explain herself. I felt puzzled by what she had done: was it no more than a gesture of friendship to Otto, or had she some motive for taking on the whole family? From her stubborn expression I knew it would be a waste of time to question her further. Only Mathilde suggested that Serge, who in his status as fiancé usually came to lunch on Sundays, should be warned in advance of the German's presence. Madeleine brushed this to one side.

'Why, I should like to know? If Serge chooses to eat with us he must accept our guests.' This was said with such vehemence and so deliberately missed the point that Mathilde abruptly subsided.

Yvonne made one final observation that night. As the clock

struck ten, Lise could be heard shuffling down the corridor to fetch her sister. Yvonne gathered up her game of patience.

'I will tell Lise that we have a guest tomorrow, but I see no need to say that he is German.' She looked sharply at us all and, taking her sister's arm, she withdrew.

Otto arrived promptly at one, this time on foot. A strong wind had for once kept us indoors and we were already assembled in the small salon drinking the usual glass of *porto* to which we were entitled before lunch on Sunday. Serge, who had arrived a few minutes earlier, was looking for Madeleine but she had not yet appeared. I felt a distinct atmosphere of unease in the room.

Otto walked in accompanied by Madeleine: she had evidently climbed some of the way to the village, perhaps even all of it, in order to meet him. I had no idea whether she had said anything to him about the reaction the previous evening to her invitation, but if she had, he appeared surprisingly at ease. He moved round, shaking hands with everyone in turn. I noticed that Serge, who came into the room a few moments later, gave him a cool look as they met, and then turned away.

We moved in to lunch. As the principal guest, Otto was placed on Tante Yvonne's right, between her and Thérèse; Madeleine and Serge were seated together at one end of the table, while Alice and Auguste were in their usual places opposite Yvonne. Father Philippe folded his hands and muttered a rapid grace.

Only seconds after we sat down, the door from the hall was

flung open with such violence that all heads turned. Lise, in her Sunday dress, stood shaking in the doorway. Her usual stoop and downcast eyes were gone. If her voice was hoarse, it was nonetheless clear.

'Yvonne,' she clutched the door handle for support, 'Yvonne, what have you done? Why is this German here? He must go.' She took a step into the room. 'I tell you, he must go,' she repeated, more quietly this time.

For a moment no one moved. Then Tante Yvonne, with a flapping motion of her arm, ordered her sister to sit, while she turned to Otto, an apology on her lips. But he was already rising from his chair. His complexion was even paler than before.

'I did not know . . . I did not realise . . .' was all he could say. He moved slowly from his place, and, with staring eyes, as if in a trance, walked past Lise towards the door.

'No! Stay!' Madeleine called, but he did not stop as she ran after him. Lise, her anger spent and with her head now bent at its habitual angle, returned slowly to the kitchen. Tante Yvonne's face had taken on an expression of great sadness. Then I saw Tante Alice: she too was motionless, but she did not trouble to keep a look of triumph from her eyes, and she was smiling quietly.

At last Tante Yvonne spoke. 'This is a day of shame for us all. I think I will go to my room now. Thérèse, please ask Lise to come to me; everyone else should finish their lunch.'

She rose, seized her cane, and hobbled out of the dining-room.

It was evening before Madeleine returned. I saw her walking quickly up the drive and moments later heard the clatter of the front door. She went straight to her mother's room and did not come down again.

The next day, Tante Yvonne told me that Madeleine was going to leave for Paris and spend the winter working there. She had rung François who had offered her a room in his apartment.

'For me it will be perhaps an even greater loss than for her mother,' said Yvonne sadly. 'Madeleine has helped me for so long and in so many ways. But I cannot force her to stay; I have seen for some time that she needs to breathe a different air, at least for a little while. I only hope she will want to come back to us soon.'

My resentment at the prospect of Madeleine's departure returned forcibly to me. Despite all she had said to me in the car I wanted someone to make a bigger effort to keep her here. But when, later in the day, Madeleine called to me from the library, where she was sorting through papers on a desk, I trotted in to her meekly enough.

'I have a favour to ask you,' she said, looking down at her lap as she often did when she felt unhappy or embarrassed. 'I must go and say goodbye to Serge this evening. Will you come too? I cannot face going on my own, and I don't think he would mind you.' I was not sure whether this was intended as a compliment but the last thing I felt able to do was refuse her.

We drove off in the Citroën in the late afternoon. There was one question which I felt I must get clear before Madeleine saw Serge.

'What happened to Otto?' I asked timidly. 'Is he still in the village?'

'Otto?' she replied distantly. 'He has left of course. How could he stay here? He should not have come: I told him so, but he's too sentimental. Anyway he learned a lesson, thanks to Tante Alice. It will be easier in Paris . . .' I felt that she was rehearsing this last remark with me before volunteering it, if cornered, to Serge, but I did not respond. Instead I stared gloomily in front of me as we took the bends round the hill at speed.

Madeleine glanced at me. 'Cheer up,' she said unexpectedly, 'it is I who have a difficult farewell to make, not you. I brought you along to encourage me, not the other way round.'

We shot between the white gateposts which marked the entrance to Serge's courtyard and jolted to a stop. Madeleine looked nervous: before getting out of the car she lit a cigarette, and drew on it once or twice before stubbing it out and smoothing down her pleated skirt with an impatient gesture.

Serge came across the courtyard towards us, his face bright with pleasure as he saw Madeleine. She looked up at him, standing almost on tiptoe in order to kiss him on the mouth before taking a step back and dropping his hand.

'Serge, I have come to say goodbye,' she said quickly, folding her hands in front of her. 'I am going to Paris for a few months.'

Serge looked astonished, then dismayed. For a moment he

was silent. At length he said pleadingly, 'Madeleine . . . why are you going now? Should we not discuss such a big step?'

She seemed to look beyond him. 'There is nothing really to discuss,' she replied coldly. 'I am sure you have noticed that I need a change. I have not been away for months; and I may not go for long.' I was suddenly reminded of Kay in the fairy-tale, whose heart was a splinter of ice.

'You should not say that unless you mean it.' For the first time Serge looked annoyed. 'And what does this mean for us? Are you trying to tell me you want to break our engagement?'

'No . . . I don't know. Please, Serge, I need to get away to think about things. You have been so patient, but please do not press me now.' For the first time she showed some emotion.

'If I did press you I know what the answer would be,' rejoined Serge unhappily. 'As long as there is a chance, I will wait for you, Madeleine. But you had better come and take leave of my mother.'

We went into the house and found the old lady seated by the window, exactly where I had seen her on my last visit. Serge bent over her.

'Mama, Madeleine has come to say *"au revoir"*. She is going away to Paris.'

The tiny woman looked up crossly. 'To Paris?' she exclaimed, as if it was the farthest end of the world, and ignoring Madeleine's presence. 'What does she want to do that for? I have always told you, my son, that the girl would let you down one day.'

'Please . . .' Madeleine stretched out her hands in a gesture of supplication, but Serge's mother was working herself into a rage.

'Why do you play with my son's affections in this way?' she cried shrilly. 'Why can you not marry him or leave him alone? You can see how unhappy you are making him.'

Serge was about to speak but Madeleine interrupted before he could do so.

'You are wrong, Tante Isabelle,' she said, breathing quickly. 'Serge can have his freedom any time he wants it. Indeed he can have it now.'

She turned away and moved down the room, shaking her fair hair back over her rigid shoulders as if defying anyone to protest. Serge walked up behind her and put his arm round her waist. For a moment she tried to move away from him, but then she allowed him to lead her outside. The old lady subsided in her chair muttering, 'No good, no good,' as she offered me her hand in farewell.

When I joined Madeleine and Serge in the courtyard they stood, facing each other, with tears on their cheeks. I jumped hastily into the car and looked fixedly away into the trees until, a few moments later, Madeleine backed sobbing into the driver's seat and started the engine. Looking round, I saw that Serge had disappeared. She took out a handkerchief, wiped her eyes and blew her nose.

'Well, that's over and so is my engagement,' she said, glancing nervously back at the door as we slid through the gates to the road. 'I didn't mean it to happen like this when we came. And I hate making Serge so unhappy but . . .' she blew out her cheeks in a gesture of relief, 'it feels right. Thank goodness I am off to Paris tomorrow.'

I looked away from her, my own eyes stinging with tears. My whole world appeared to be dissolving in unhappiness. Sensing my misery, Madeleine took one hand from the wheel and put it round my shoulders.

'Now come on,' she said quietly. Her eyes were still damp and the lids were swollen. 'You are going away too. You have to grow up and so, after all, do I.'

Madeleine left for the station the next morning. She declined all offers to accompany her in the car although everyone rose to be in time to say goodbye to her on the steps when Joseph appeared behind the wheel of the Citroën at nine o'clock. She descended the long staircase from Tante Yvonne's room carrying two small suitcases and looking, I thought, prettier than ever, her blonde hair crowned inadequately by a beret and falling over the collar of a long, dark green, closely cut overcoat.

After embracing everyone in turn she came down the steps to where I was standing awkwardly by the car door.

'Promise me', I said defiantly, 'that you will be here when I come back.'

It was an imprecise and, I realised, unreasonable request, but Madeleine paused and appeared to take it seriously.

'I promise, of course,' she replied gravely, and then with a quick movement she slipped into the car and shut the door. As Joseph moved off, the aunts clustered on the steps, waving.

But I ran back into the house.

* * *

Only a week later it was my own turn to leave for England. The train was due to halt at the village early in the morning and Tante Yvonne asked me to come to her room to say goodbye. I found her sitting fully dressed in a deep armchair reading some letters. She looked up at me with a humorous expression as I stood dolefully before her.

'You are not, I hope, returning to imprisonment, although what I have read about your schools makes me wonder!'

She smiled gently. 'You have, I think, learnt many things this summer as part of our family. From now on you will always have a place here. But please remember one lesson which I too have had to learn this year.'

She gestured at the rows of photographs hanging by the bed.

'I have fought all my days to hold my family together and to keep this house alive. Perhaps I have tried too much. For we must each of us lead our own life, and if I have been saddened to see Bob and Madeleine leave I know in my heart that they have made the right choice. I will have succeeded when they decide to come back; and the same will be true of you as well.'

'But I do not want to go at all,' I exclaimed, suddenly panic-stricken. 'Couldn't I stay, Tante Yvonne? I could go to school somewhere near here . . .' My voice trailed away as I realised the absurdity of what I was saying.

'That is flattering for us, and I am very touched. But what would they think at home if I tried to keep you?' She gave the little dry laugh I knew so well. 'No, it is right that you should grow up an Englishman, but I think that henceforth a part of your heart will always belong to France. Now you must go, my child, but I shall be waiting for you to return to me.'

She took my hand in both of hers and looked up at me with a curious expression, half-solemn, half-smiling, as I bent to kiss her. For a moment she held on to me and I could see the affection in her eyes. Then I turned quickly away and went back down the long staircase to the others who were waiting for me below.

## XIV  Tante Yvonne

The headmaster pushed a telegram at me across the table and cleared his throat. 'Bad news, I'm afraid. Are you close to your aunt?' I looked down at the scrap of grey paper on which was pasted a typewritten message: '*Tante Yvonne gravement malade. Viens vite si tu peux.* Madeleine.' Without speaking, I nodded. The headmaster cracked his long fingers.

'Of course we only allow leave of absence for the illness or decease of immediate relatives, but under the circumstances . . . I have spoken to your father and he is happy for you to go. I understand you have no difficulty in travelling alone.'

I nodded again. It was early April, and after a long, bitter winter when for weeks on end the ground had been frozen hard as iron, there was a touch of warmth in the air. For some time I had been vaguely disquieted by an absence of news from the house. Since I had left Tante Yvonne had written to me every month, sometimes just a postcard with a blurred picture of the village or the house and a few lines scrawled on the back, at others a letter which I would carry with me for days trying to decipher her hooked and sprawling handwriting. She also was in the habit of slipping into the envelopes of her letters a miniature *médaille miraculeuse* representing the Virgin, of which she appeared to have an inexhaustible supply. The last missive had spoken not of herself but of Oncle Auguste:

> Our brother has been too weak to travel this year and has spent the winter months here with us, mostly, I fear, in his room. We are hoping that his strength will return with the spring. We miss you around the house and count on seeing you again for the Easter festivities.

The little train stopped at every station and wayside platform on its way across the plain to the hills where the village lay. As we drew into the larger stations sepulchral voices, whose tone seemed in keeping with the mood of my journey, recited through loudspeakers the name of the town and the train's remaining itinerary. At the smaller halts there was only silence, almost a hush, punctuated by the slamming of a door as a passenger alighted. With a silent lurch the train then glided forward again, accelerating steadily until we were rattling across roads and through pastureland or flat expanses of plough stretching on either side to the horizon. We journeyed under a sullen sky that occasionally closed down upon us with great bands of mist, always signalled by prolonged whistles from the engine. I was impatient to arrive but clammy with apprehension at the thought of the emotion and loss which was, minute by minute, coming nearer. My only companion in the carriage, an old lady in black, slept in a far corner, a basket of provisions by her side. I felt grateful for her silent presence.

Eventually my eyes found what I had been steadily scanning the horizon for: a curve rising from the plain which, as we approached, took on the contours of a chain of hills, the nearest and largest being crowned by the walls and houses of the village. The sight of this familiar landscape should have filled me with excitement and an impatience to arrive. But I had to force myself to stand up and reach for my suitcase in the swaying carriage rather than sink back in the corner of my seat, and let the train carry me past the station.

I jumped from the high step to a deserted platform below. Dragging my suitcase down after me, I walked through the booking hall to the forecourt as the train disappeared along the track and the crossing gates opened behind it. The Citroën was waiting behind them and now lurched forward. Madeleine sprang out, put her arms on my shoulders, and kissed me on both cheeks.

'You have grown,' she said. Her fair hair was dishevelled and there were dark shadows under her eyes. 'I am glad you have come in time. Poor Tante Yvonne is sinking fast, but she asked this morning where you were. She has been in bed for six weeks now and in the last ten days she has begun to drift away from us. The doctor does not want to do any more for her. He says that she is too weak and that it is better to let her go quietly.'

We drove round the hill, up the cobbled road running past the property and through the familiar white brick gateway to the house. Looking up from the drive I could see that the curtains to Tante Yvonne's room were drawn. As I came into the hall, Lise, her figure bent almost in two, was shuffling down the stairs. She stood on the bottom step and embraced me.

'She is sleeping,' she croaked, 'but you must go in now. We never know when she will wake.'

I ran up the stairs and slipped into Tante Yvonne's room. A fire was burning in the big hearth, and a lamp stood on a little table near the bed, by the light of which Florence was quietly sewing. Tante Yvonne lay motionless on her back, her eyes closed, one hand on the sheet. Florence beckoned me forward.

'Come and sit with her,' she said in a low voice, gathering up her work and retreating to the fireplace. 'The *curé* is on his way from the village with the extreme unction, for the doctor is not sure that she will last the night.'

I sat down in Florence's chair, suddenly recalling that Tante Yvonne had once told me that she had been born in this room; now, more than eighty years later, she was dying in it. As I gazed down at the old lady I longed to touch her hand and tell her I had come back to her as she had asked, but I dared not disturb her rest. Her breathing was shallow and, alarmingly, seemed occasionally to stop altogether before resuming with a gasp for air. Suddenly, her right hand moved: it twitched and, with two fingers extended, rose and fell on the white sheet, as if beating time.

'They are singing,' she muttered; then she opened her hooded eyes and stared at me, at first I thought without recognition. After a long silence she appeared to be trying to speak. I leaned forward. 'Dear child,' she whispered, and her eyes closed again.

There was a rustle on the stairs and the priest came noiselessly into the room, carrying a small leather box which he placed on the mantelpiece. Behind him followed Father Philippe and then Lise, Thérèse and Auguste leaning heavily on a stick. Tante Alice, Florence and Madeleine brought up the rear. They all stood quietly at the end of the bed as the priest prepared himself; then, sitting on the chair by her pillow, he bent over and ministered to Tante Yvonne. He spoke a few sentences in Latin and drew responses from Father Philippe as the others closed their eyes in prayer. It was a dignified little ceremony, conducted without an exaggerated display of grief.

When he had finished I accompanied the *curé* downstairs.

'Well, that's it,' he said almost cheerfully, 'she can go in peace now.' He sat on his motorcycle and kicked the starter. 'But please ring me when there is any change and I will come at once.'

He roared away along the drive. I walked down to the lake.

The little green boat had been put back in the water and lay moored to the landing-stage, a sure sign that winter was considered over. I slipped the moorings and rowed slowly away from the shore. At the far end, where the reeds marched into the water, some moorhens swam in and out, ignoring my presence. I looked up, over the swell of the rising fields to the church tower which seemed itself to be moving against a line of fleecy clouds passing behind it. When I shipped my oars the boat drifted past the island where in summer the children loved to picnic; now it looked damp and neglected, but the mass of bluebells which carpeted the wood on one side of the lake had spawned some patches of blue on the island, too. As the current pushed the boat towards the wood, Christian came silently out from the trees and stood on the bank watching me. I raised a hand in greeting and shouted to him that Tante Yvonne was now very weak.

'I know,' he said, 'I feel it here.' He put his hand on his heart.

It was a long evening. The aunts took turns in their uninterrupted vigil at Tante Yvonne's bedside, while the rest of us sat listlessly in the salon, disinclined to talk, our thoughts preoccupied by the life ebbing away in the room overhead. Tante Yvonne's playing cards and her lettercase lay undisturbed by her usual chair which stood empty although the little room was crowded. By the flickering light from the hearth I looked in turn at the craggy features of Tante Alice, bent over her work, the serene, round face of Florence, Oncle Auguste biting his moustache as he struggled to roll a cigarette, while next to him Thérèse distractedly turned the pages of a heavy book. Behind the desk in the corner Madeleine was writing some notes, her hair falling over her face, her shoes kicked to one side. I closed my eyes, and tired out by the journey and the emotions of the day, fell asleep.

When I woke some time later the room was empty. The fire had burned down and Florence was gently pressing my arm.

'We have to go upstairs again now,' she said. 'I am afraid this is the end.'

Arm in arm, we ascended the staircase and looking down I saw Zoë, Joseph and Christian clustered anxiously in the hall. The door to Tante Yvonne's room stood wide open. The priest was kneeling by one side of the bed, holding Yvonne's hand, while he recited Hail Marys uninterruptedly. On the other side Lise stood looking sadly but quietly down on her sister whose breathing was now coming in short gasps. A few moments later it stopped altogether. The little priest bent over Tante Yvonne and folded her hands. Then he stood up and turned round.

'She has left us,' he said.

It was late when I awoke the next morning. Florence had taken me to my room, leaving Tante Yvonne's two sisters and Auguste alone with her. As I lay in bed I heard a toll from the church bell in the village, a single echoing boom to mark each passing minute. Below I could sense an atmosphere of quiet activity in the house: people moved ceaselessly up and down the stairs and strange voices conversed in the hall.

I slipped down the back staircase and went to look for

Madeleine: she was sitting with Florence and Thérèse in the library, already deeply involved in arrangements for the funeral. I listened admiringly as they dealt briskly and competently with the complexities of what had to be done. Already the telephone was beginning to ring and callers were arriving, unbidden, to leave flowers and offer their condolences.

At midday they brought Tante Yvonne downstairs in an open coffin, which was placed on an improvised bier in the little salon. They had dressed her in purple, one of her favourite colours. The drive was now thronged with villagers, farmers in hastily donned dark suits and neighbours in ancient cars, all of whom filed through the hall and paused at the coffin in a gesture of respect for the lady most had known all their lives, and who until recently had seemed indestructible. For some time I stood at the back of the room watching the procession of mourners, some familiar, some unknown, until Madeleine came in search of me and, taking me by the hand, led me back into the library. Auguste sat crumpled in an armchair looking vacantly out of the window.

'Oncle Auguste has a favour to ask you: he would like you to be one of the bearers at the funeral. Am I right?' Madeleine looked at him and he nodded silently. For the present he seemed incapable of speech. 'The others will be Joseph, Christian and Serge. Bob will not be back from his ship in time. Serge will come here this evening and tell you all what to do.'

The house was kept busy over the next few days as it filled up with relatives while preparations were completed for the funeral and the big reception which was to follow. But this activity could not mask a sense of loss which seemed, if anything, to grow as time passed. Without Tante Yvonne's authority and presence, the smallest decisions had become hard to take. I wandered from room to room, feeling increasingly desolate, and conscious that the person who had only recently become the centre of my world had now just as quickly gone forever.

On the day of the burial the aunts, dressed in deep mourning, gathered in the hall. A procession of hired cars stood in front of the house, led by a great hearse in which we, the four pall-bearers, gently placed the coffin. I noticed how small and light it was. The great church bell was tolling as we drove slowly up the twisting road to the village square. To my surprise, standing at the front of the crowd below the church steps were Rémy and the members of his municipal council, their hats removed, their expressions solemn. Rémy came forward, shook hands with Lise and Tante Thérèse, and embraced Florence as we carried Tante Yvonne, her coffin covered with a simple cloth, through a packed congregation to a table in front of the altar, where the village priest and a monk dressed in white were waiting for us; Father Philippe hovered uneasily behind them.

When we had put the coffin down, the monk mounted the steps of the ornate pulpit, his white robe dragging after him. There was a pause while he looked down at us.

'Friends, brothers and sisters in Christ,' he began, 'I, Father Xavier, am here today to say farewell with you to the greatest ady and truest friend that I believe any of us has known. Her life has reflected the history of France in her generation, but it has also been a life of self-sacrifice, the sacrifice of the husband and family of her own which she could have had, for the sake of a far larger circle of family and friends.

'Each one of us will recall an act of kindness or a word of advice from Mademoiselle Yvonne, and it is the total of such memories which represents for us a person's life. As long as memories of her endure Yvonne will stay among the living. Today I shall not recount to you the story of her life: I would prefer that as we pray for her soul, each of us remembers what she did for us individually. And to help you in this I will tell you how she once performed a great service for me.'

He paused for a moment and gazed over our heads to the back of the church, as if recollecting a distant past.

'It was the end of the Great War, and as I lay wounded in hospital I felt a strong vocation for the Church. Yet like many who had been through those terrible times and had lost so many relatives and friends, I was confused about the way ahead. So I turned to Yvonne, whom I had known as a child, and she invited me to stay at the château. One evening she took me to the chapel in the grounds, which many of you know and where we shall be burying her today, and for many hours we talked about the choices before me. She did not seek to influence me, but by dawn I knew what I had to do. As we returned to the house Yvonne pointed to the sky where, I remember, some clouds had formed the shape of a cross.

'"There is our sign," she said. "Now I have to ask you a

favour. If you return here to Flanders, will you take my confession?" And so, nearly every month for more than thirty years, Yvonne has visited me at the monastery to discuss her problems and find absolution. I, too, have been able to share my own thoughts and troubles with her. It is my great sadness but privilege to accompany her today to her body's last resting place.'

He descended the pulpit and knelt for a moment by the coffin before walking up the chancel as the choir began to sing.

At the end of the service Father Xavier led the way back through the crowded church to the great doors giving on to the square. We drove slowly down to the house; and the procession halted in the drive, opposite the gravel path which led through the woods to the chapel. Weak rays of spring sunshine made pools on the grass as we bore the coffin to the entrance of the chapel where a flagstone covering a vault had been raised. As Joseph and Christian clambered down into the tomb, Lise shuffled forward and laid a small bunch of flowers on the top of the coffin. Her lips were moving as if in prayer, and two tears ran slowly down her cheeks as she made this last gesture of farewell. The flowers rolled forward but somehow stayed in place as Serge and I lowered the coffin to be inserted on one of the shelves in the vault, and Father Xavier recited a last prayer from within the chapel.

For the first time I was able to look back at the crowd who stood in a semi-circle around the entrance, dressed almost identically in black. Madeleine came forward and put an arm round my shoulder.

'Your train leaves in an hour, so I will take you back to the house,' she said. 'The family will stay here for some time and you must get ready.'

As we walked back down the path more people, having arrived by car, were hurrying towards the chapel. We went into the empty house and climbed the stairs to my room. Madeleine sat heavily down on the bed; she tucked her slim legs underneath her and leaned back against the wall as she watched me assembling my clothes in a suitcase. Then she turned her head and stared through the window at the distant horizon.

'Before you go I will tell you something that I have mentioned to no one so far, not even my mother. Can you keep a secret?'

'Of course I can.' How many times had I been asked that question since I first set foot in the house!

'It happened three weeks ago, just after I came back from Paris. I was sitting alone with Tante Yvonne when suddenly she woke, restless and agitated. She began to talk about the house and Lise and what was to become of everything. Then she took my hand and said: "Madeleine, will you promise to come back and take charge? Only you can do it. Give me this promise and I can go in peace."'

Madeleine sighed. 'I was already feeling guilty that I had gone away when I did. What else could I do but give my word? And with Tante Yvonne I knew I had to mean it. Of course she realised that as well: she looked so content afterwards, everyone noticed that, but she never said a word to me again about my promise, nor did she speak of it to the others. I keep asking myself whether she realised what her request meant. She wanted me to follow her along a path which she herself had taken sixty years ago; it sounds simple but I am not Tante Yvonne and the world is different today as well.'

She tried, not very successfully, to smile. 'I will tell them all tonight that I am leaving Paris and coming home. They will say how happy and grateful they are, but they will wonder what has happened. In one way they will be right, I did not have an easy time of it. Otto came at first but he left quickly when he saw that we had after all little in common. Nor was living with François and Chantal so easy, as my mother warned me. For the rest, I will tell you another time. Meanwhile here I am back again with dear Serge expecting me to marry him and no doubt live happily ever after.'

So, I thought, at the last moment Tante Yvonne had been unable to resist giving fate a nudge. I recalled how she had told me when we last spoke that Madeleine should be left to decide for herself whether and when to return to the family; but I could not repress a self-centred feeling of gratitude for what she had done.

Madeleine glanced at her watch. 'You must not miss your train. I will fetch the car while you make your farewells.'

They were walking slowly up to the house from the chapel as we came down the stairs. On the steps I embraced Florence, Thérèse and Tante Alice in turn, but of Lise there was no sign. As I looked round for her she emerged from the kitchen carrying a blue envelope which I saw had my name scrawled on it in Tante Yvonne's hand. Lise's eyes were swollen and red, but she succeeded in giving me a smile as she passed the envelope to me.

'Yvonne asked me to let you have this after the funeral; you may open it later. And', she drew herself up a little straighter as if conscious that there was a new mantle on her shoulders, 'please let us know when you are returning. Your room is waiting for you.' I bent down and kissed her awkwardly on her forehead. Then I fled to Madeleine in the car.

As we moved down the drive, two figures emerged from the path in the trees and turned towards the house. They were Oncle Auguste, leaning heavily on his stick and supported on one side by Christian. Auguste wore a heavy black overcoat, and a hat which might once have been an 'Anthony Eden'. Madeleine stopped the car and I alighted to shake hands with each of them. Auguste looked me up and down.

'You are growing,' he remarked, as if noticing my presence for the first time. 'Come back soon, my boy.' And with this instruction and a 'Forward!' to Christian, he moved on.

We drove into the station forecourt just before the crossing gates closed behind us; I could hear the train approaching.

'We must be quick,' said Madeleine, pulling my suitcase out of the car.

I clambered into the train and she stood smiling up at me from the platform below. There was much I wanted to say: that I was so happy she was after all coming back; that I loved her; that I would return as soon as I could escape again from school. But perhaps fortunately the equal intensity of my unhappiness at leaving and my joy over her return prevented me from giving coherent expression to what I felt. I could do no more than smile back as, leaning from the window, I despairingly thrust a hand towards her. When the train moved off she took a step forward and then stood, shielding her eyes against the sun, until we turned a bend in the track. Exhausted and empty I fell back in my seat.

Then I remembered Tante Yvonne's envelope. I found it crumpled in my pocket, and hastily tore it open. The note was not dated, and the writing sprawled across the page in lines that were in places almost diagonal.

My child,

By the time you read this I shall no longer be with you but I beg you not to grieve. You are at the start of your life while I have come to the end of mine. This is only natural and one day you too will I hope look back as I have done over many years of experience and happiness.

My journey has been a long one. But as I believe you have come to understand, I have always struggled to keep us all together in the face of the storms and tragedies afflicting the world around us. You should never forget that a strong and united family is a bottomless well of love and support. My only true sadness is that I have had no children of my own: perhaps if your grandfather Jack had after all returned to me things would have been different, but I have never regretted what is past and I beg you not to do so either. You will have disappointments as well as pleasures in your life and you must above all learn to use them to your advantage and know how to turn the pages of the future.

From the moment that you came to us last summer I knew that you, too, belonged here. You must always look on this house as your home. I am so happy to have known Jack's grandson before leaving for a place where I hope I will be allowed to watch over all those whom I love. Return here soon, my dear child, and you will fulfil a last wish of your affectionate,

Tante Yvonne

I looked through the carriage window. The village was no longer visible but I could still see the hill and thought I could make out, lower down, a patch of trees within which the house must be standing. The sun had finally won its fight with the clouds; it was turning into a fine afternoon. 'Just the day for the big walk,' Oncle Auguste would have said.

# Epilogue

No memories are more vivid than those of our childhood and early youth. Each new experience has the force of revelation, all the more striking because there is little or nothing with which to compare it. For this reason certain episodes of our past will always stand out with extraordinary clarity, even if passing time gradually distorts and erodes them.

I have often been asked to what extent the people I have depicted really existed and the events I have described truly occurred. For this book was written after an interval of half a century during which I travelled widely and much happened in my life. I can only say that when, after such a lapse in time, I set out to recall that period in my youth, it reappeared as in a dream, complete but surreal. Others have seen what I wrote as somehow suspended between recollection and fiction. For me it results rather from the play of imagination on memory, the whole forming the best picture I could give of experiences which have over the years proved unforgettable.

The unique aspects of this moment in my boyhood were, in retrospect, related as much to the process of growing up as to the novel and colourful environment into which I was thrown. Although there may be no such thing as a normal family – indeed Tolstoy's proposition that 'All happy families resemble one another; but each unhappy family is unhappy in its own way' is in my view highly questionable – by the time I was thirteen I was conscious that we were not entirely like other families. My parents' marriage nearly broke up during the long years of the war: my father, previously a Classics don at Cambridge, was from the onset of hostilities sequestered within the secret world of the code-breaking communications centre at Bletchley Park about which he was forbidden to speak at the time or later even to his wife; this, ironically, seemingly inhibiting his ability to communicate more generally with the rest of us. At this distance it is not always easy to understand the intense pressures to which the Bletchley teams were subjected for prolonged periods, pressures which left a number of those concerned psychologically scarred, as damaged as if they had suffered serious physical wounds.

My mother, a frustrated intellectual who today would no doubt have pursued a successful career within the educational establishment, had few maternal instincts and, prompted by my father's absence, also sought work outside the home, not, one suspects, without a sense of relief. With no professional qualifications, she first devoted herself to reorganising and running a local library; then, in a combined fit of social conscience and patriotism, she volunteered to join an assembly line at Shorts, the aircraft manufacturers, returning home each evening exhausted by this physical labour to take over from a nanny whose husband was a prisoner-of-war. Many years later I came across a letter from her which explained graphically what I had instinctively felt at the time. Writing to a close male friend in 1942, she speaks of her desolation that my father had fallen out of love with her, and that this had 'almost broken my heart. I don't really do anything except try to work myself into a stupor so as to think and feel less . . . If your lover dies you can at least live in the past, but when this happens both the past and the future go together.'

Despite this emotional rupture, at the end of the war my parents purchased a substantial house in Hertfordshire and re-established the nuclear family. My father resumed his academic career, but the two withdrew from each other into their separate worlds. No doubt the conventions of the time dictated that in the absence of flagrant infidelity on one side or the other they stay together; they may also have stuck it out for the sake of their children – I had a younger brother. Even so, the house scarcely felt like a home. It was a cold and empty place, with few friends to enliven us, both my parents preferring an environment of books and, to my youthful mind, frigid intellectual exchanges to the more complicated and demanding world of personal relationships.

It is perhaps scarcely surprising that I became a withdrawn, bookish child who did not find it easy to make friends either at home or at the eccentric, privately owned boarding school to which I had been entrusted. Not for me the rough and tumble of a sprawling family life, nor the give and take of easy companionship with boys of my own age. I was more ignorant of the wider world than was, I think, customary even for boys who spent two-thirds of each year closeted in their schools. My parents were suspicious of, even hostile to, much of what went on outside their immediate circle, an attitude I absorbed in the shape of an unusual degree of apprehension about life in general. At the same time I acquired the habit of minutely observing new faces and storing away experiences for future use. But I had grown no hard shell with which to confront the outside world, and when I was unexpectedly – and in retrospect somewhat surprisingly – informed that I was to be despatched for several months to live among strangers in France I was more alarmed than exhilarated at the prospect.

The interest and affection with which I was greeted by my French hosts, for which I only understood the underlying reasons some time after my arrival, did much to dispel my initial worries. Not surprisingly, the absence of a companion of my own age did not concern me; I had never needed one. As it was, I quickly became involved in the life of the house and found it a new and pleasurable experience to be a focus of attention. I was not just a spectator, but an actor in the play unfolding around me; and in this role I grew up fast. Nothing, of course, was threatening: there were no sudden deaths, no violence or disrupting events which are often associated with a leap from childhood to maturity. But the need to adapt to the, for me, bewildering number of people daily surrounding me, and my frequent involvement in situations where an outsider such as myself provided a natural ear or could even act as a catalyst, instilled in me a sense of self-confidence which had hitherto been wholly unfamiliar.

If my self-confidence was nonetheless restrained, this was because at least in part in those months I imagined myself in love for the first time in my life, with all the timidity and fears commonly associated with this state of being. Of course my feelings were immature and, as my parents would have been the first to say, ill-directed, the object of my affections being six years older than myself and belonging to the unknowable world of adulthood. But they were nonetheless intense, and while I had the good sense to conceal it as best I could, my infatuation for Madeleine gave me the conviction of having become irrevocably bound to the whole family. Indeed I could no longer envisage belonging anywhere else.

When Tante Yvonne died soon after my first visit I experienced an acute sense of loss. She was the centre of a world whose discovery had changed my life, and I grieved as much for myself as I did for her. Moreover I felt that the special regard in which, for her own reasons, she had held me could never be replaced. For her family, it was as if the winding spring of a watch had broken. The routine of the house continued, but the sense that someone was controlling and guiding daily life was gone; while the embodiment of nearly a century of history, as it had in diverse ways affected this family, had vanished with her.

Yet in the early years after her death I returned again and again to the house. I remained under its spell as school gave way to university and university to the junior ranks of the diplomatic service. Whenever possible I would come back to occupy the room on the top floor that I had been given on my first visit, where pictures I had once found in the attic still hung on the walls. I corresponded regularly with Florence, but when I was in my early twenties she, Lise and Auguste died in quick succession – the latter succumbing to dementia – and the link was broken. Bob did not long survive his mother: he suffered a heart attack, dying in a Paris restaurant while inspecting the bill after a good lunch; a not uncharacteristic end, one felt.

And Madeleine? After we said goodbye that afternoon at the station I was to have no more than occasional glimpses of her, for the following year she escaped with the connivance of her mother to work in a town in Normandy, living with relatives and subsequently marrying a local businessman. She had three children before dying of a lung disease at an untimely age. Serge too married, but he did not survive early middle age. Longevity, it seemed, was the prerogative of an earlier generation.

Yet the next generation was not far behind, in the shape of a network of young cousins who had been no more than infants playing in nurseries and sandpits during my first summer. They now held on to the house, having been determined to find the resources to maintain it. It was as if the house was unwilling to let go of them, and while the farms and cottages were sold off to their tenants, the world behind the gates remained intact. True, the property was apparently now often deserted in the long winter months, but each year with the arrival of spring it came alive, now the focus of new lives, of which from time to time I heard faint echoes.

Meanwhile my own career was marked by a restlessness which may have owed something to the different worlds I had navigated in my youth. Certainly the peripatetic life of the diplomat, if not always kind to my family, suited my temperament, but after some years as an Ambassador I felt the need for a new start and resigned, returning to London to plunge into the unfamiliar world of investment banking; this to be followed a decade later by the chairmanship of the British arm of one of America's leading defence companies. Maybe these changes were not altogether career-enhancing, but they satisfied an emotional need to experience new environments and test myself in them. In the background was always the urge to write, though I never had enough confidence in my talents to turn to writing as a profession.

* * *

On the eve of the first publication of this book I found myself on a motorway travelling towards the Channel ports and realised that I was no more than fifteen minutes' drive from the village. I had not wanted to return to the house during the writing. After so long an absence I feared that inevitable changes in the place over the years and the, to me, new faces of the occupants would smudge the images in my mind, tearing at the fabric of memory. But now my work was done. On impulse I turned off the motorway and within moments I was climbing the hill to the village, then driving down the still cobbled road which led to the entrance to the property.

It was a clear day, of a kind you often encounter in Flanders in the autumn, and although it was mid-afternoon the sun was already low on the horizon. The trees were turning red and gold, awaiting the first frost to start losing their leaves. As I turned into the drive, past the familiar white brick pillars, I sought unsuccessfully to measure the lapse of time, for outwardly everything appeared as before: the oak tree still pointed at the same alarming angle towards the chapel, the rhododendron bushes were still in place, larger than ever but well trimmed; and the expanse of grass in front of the house, never a lawn, was still roughly mown. The shutters were open, the house clearly occupied. I sat for a moment in the car wondering who would be there and how to explain my unexpected appearance.

I pushed open the glass door, the panes rattling as they always had. The house was intensely silent and I glanced at the broad staircase, half expecting to see Tante Yvonne making her usual slow backwards descent to the hall. I walked through to the long dining-room: it was brightly lit by the sun but deserted, and the French windows on to the terrace steps stood wide open. Returning to the hall I rang the handbell which stood in its familiar place. A door opened on the floor above, and a voice asked who was there. Before I could answer I heard steps on the landing and a slim, fair-haired woman in her late thirties appeared at the head of the stairs and began to descend. Looking up, I felt a moment of immediate recognition without at once knowing why, but by the time she reached me I knew who she must be.

Once she, in her turn, had understood who I was, Madeleine's daughter Nadia – her eldest child – greeted me warmly, then took me into the sunshine to sit on the terrace.

There she pressed me to describe Tante Yvonne and the aunts and uncles she had known only through her mother's stories, which after an interval of more than thirty years she barely remembered. As she spoke and laughed I saw Madeleine again, and almost without thinking I told Nadia that the house as I had found it many years ago was about to live again in a book which would shortly appear under my name. Then I paused, nervous. I was suddenly conscious of an invasion of privacy, even the abduction of the family's past. But Nadia made light of my concerns. 'What a present!' she exclaimed. 'You will be giving back to us memories we all thought we had lost long since.' I felt relieved; but then, thinking of my description of Madeleine's turbulent weeks that summer, not wholly reassured. I could only hope that in view of Nadia's distant memory of her mother – she had been only five when Madeleine died – her predominant reaction to those remote events would be one of curiosity.

As we talked the shadows crept along the terrace, and the swallows swooped over the grass, until we were interrupted by the animated appearance of a boy, Nadia's son, who had been fishing in the lake. As he ran on into the house, she told me of the decision she and her lawyer husband had taken that summer: with the enthusiastic approval of their cousins they had agreed to move from Normandy in order to occupy the property here permanently. They had realised that it needed a continual presence, she explained, and they had both concluded that this step was right for their family as well as for the house.

I at once thought of Madeleine's broken promise to Tante

Yvonne. No need to mention it, I reflected, her daughter would read about it soon enough. After all, the fulfilment of this promise had only been deferred by a generation, no more than the blink of an eye in the long passage of time.

Michael Jenkins
London, June 2010

SLIGHTLY FOXED PAPERBACKS

Adrian Bell, *Corduroy*
Ysenda Maxtone Graham, *Mr Tibbits's Catholic School*
Diana Holman-Hunt, *My Grandmothers and I*
Michael Jenkins, *A House in Flanders*
Priscilla Napier, *A Late Beginner*
Rosemary Sutcliff, *Blue Remembered Hills*

Slightly Foxed Paperbacks are published by
Slightly Foxed Ltd. For more information please contact us at
53 Hoxton Square, London N1 6PB
tel 020 7033 0258 · fax 0870 1991245
all@foxedquarterly.com · www.foxedquarterly.com